SIMPLE HOUSEHOLD AND AUTOMOTIVE ELECTRICAL TESTING

by
William Barden, Jr.

A DIVISION OF TANDY CORPORATION
FT. WORTH. TEXAS 76102

Editing: Janet Laurie
Artist: Mike Chiavetta

First Edition
First Printing - 1990

9   8   7   6   5   4   3   2   1

Table of Contents

Preface

There's an amazing number of things that you as an average homeowner can do to test household electrical circuits, electrical appliances, and automotive electrical circuits. You can save a great deal of money by doing it yourself, rather than paying for expensive repair or service. The tests in this book use a few simple tools, most of which cost $5 to $15 - a far cry from a high service bill (and the tools can be used again and again). But don't you need to know something about electrical repair? Not really. This book provides all of the instructions you need to do such things as

- Locate and replace a bad switch

- Replace a bad wall outlet

- Test your car battery

- Test and repair your automatic sprinkler system

- Replace fuses in your home

- Repair doorbell wiring

- Repair lamp wiring

- Determine the problem with a dead socket

- Replace car fuses

- Test telephone lines

- and more...

Simple Household and Automotive Testing contains chapters on all phases of household and automotive circuits.

Chapter 1 describes common batteries and the most cost effective types. It also describes how to use inexpensive battery testers.

Chapter 2 describes how to test the continuity of many different types of wires, including audio cables, speaker lines, television cables, sprinkler control lines, and outside lighting.

Puzzled by your fuses and circuit breakers? Chapter 3 has the answers to that array of fuses or circuit breakers.

Chapter 4 describes a very handy electrical tester called a multitester, which can be used to test home wiring voltages, continuity and resistance of wires, and currents. Multitesters can be purchased for as little as $15.

Would you like to do simple electrical repairs around the house? Chapter 5 tells you how to locate and repair troubles in wall outlets and switches safely and easily.

Low-voltage wiring is used in doorbells, sprinkler systems, outdoor decorative lighting, and small power supplies. Chapter 6 tells you how to repair some of these items.

Chapter 7 describes how to repair plugs and extension cords, lamps, and fluorescent lights and also describes simple tests on home appliances.

Chapter 8 describes automotive tests and repairs you can make, starting with your vehicle's battery and continuing through headlights, taillights, interior lights, and flasher units.

A glossary of electrical terms completes the book and provides a reference to some of those mysterious buzzwords you'll encounter when working with electrical circuits.

Chapter 1
Testing Batteries

Batteries are found in watches, calculators, hearing aids, cameras, flash-lights, tv remote controls, camcorders, portable telephones, computers, portable televisions, radios, tape recorders, smoke detectors, and hundreds of other items. You don't have to be an electrical engineer to test batteries - no knowledge of electricity is really required. Also, there's no shock hazard with batteries found in consumer products. You can handle 1.5-, 6-, and 9-volt batteries with your bare hands. It's only when special-purpose batteries with voltage ratings over 30 or 40 volts are involved that you have to be concerned about shocks.

Precautions to observe with batteries are these:

• Never throw batteries into a fire. Extreme heat might cause them to explode.

• Watch for occasional leakage of battery acid. This is no longer a major problem. However, if you do encounter slight leakage, wash your hands quickly and thoroughly and take care not to get the material into your eyes.

Types of Batteries

There are four very common types of batteries in general use: carbon-zinc, zinc-chloride, alkaline, and nickel-cadmium batteries. Their life and cost in-crease in that order.

Carbon-zinc batteries are usually the lowest-priced batteries to be sold in stores. They are not good for extreme heat or cold and don't have a long shelf life. (Shelf life is the time batteries stay on the shelves before they are used.) They should be used in equipment that does not require a great deal of energy. They are poor for high-current devices that use light bulbs or motors but fine for flashlight use. If your inexpensive batteries run down quickly, it might pay to invest in a better grade.

Zinc-chloride batteries are usually sold as "Heavy Duty" batteries. They cost about 50% percent more than the least expensive batteries. On the other hand, they last about 50% longer than the least expensive grade and are better at low temperatures.

Alkaline batteries are the best grade of throw-away batteries. They are usually sold as "Alkaline" batteries. They cost about three times more than general-purpose carbon-zinc batteries but last about seven or eight times as long. Alkaline batteries have a high capacity, are better at high and low temperatures, and have a long shelf life.

Nickel-cadmium batteries are sold as "ni-cds" batteries. Unlike the other batteries mentioned above, they are *rechargeable* batteries. When they run down, they can be put into a battery recharger and restored to life. Ni-cds cost about six times more than general-purpose carbon-zinc batteries and don't last as long as alkaline batteries. However, they can be reused dozens of times.

The batteries above are the most common types for general use. However, there are many other types as well. Mercuric-oxide ("mercury") batteries are used in electronic watches, calculators, and hearing aids. They are the "button" type of batteries about the size of a large, thick coat button.

Silver-oxide batteries are also button cells. They are also used in some types of watches.

Lithium-manganese ("lithium") batteries are used to power watches with liquid crystal displays (the gray or green type of digital display). They have a flat button shape.

Zinc-air batteries are used in pagers, hearing aids, and personal medical electronics. They are a fatter button battery.

Batteries come in many different shapes and sizes. Some common sizes and designations are shown in Figure 1-1.

A Little More About Batteries

Batteries store electrical energy. Generally, the larger the battery size, the more energy that can be stored. Batteries supply electrical *current* at a certain *voltage*. Current can be thought of as being similar to water flowing through a hose. Voltage can be thought of as the water pressure forcing current through the hose. Some devices, such as flashlights and portable tape recorders, require a great deal of current and run down batteries quickly. Other devices, such as remote controls for televisions and video cassette recorders, require very little current and do not run down batteries very quickly at all.

In addition to material used and physical size, batteries are rated in voltage and the amount of energy they store. The voltage of a battery is the amount of "force" required to push the current through a device. Common voltages are 1.5 volts (flashlight cells), 6 volts (lantern batteries), 9 volts (transistor radios and test equipment), and 12 volts (camcorders). A higher voltage battery isn't better - it's just designed to work with a certain device at that voltage. Replace batteries with ones of the same voltage.

The amount of energy stored is often not given for common batteries, such as A, AA, B, C, and D cells. Batteries for high-current requirements, such as camcorders, are sometimes rated in *mAh* - milliampere-hours. The higher this rating, the longer the battery will last. A mAh rating of 2000 mAh means that the battery will last twice as long as one with a rating of 1000 mAh.

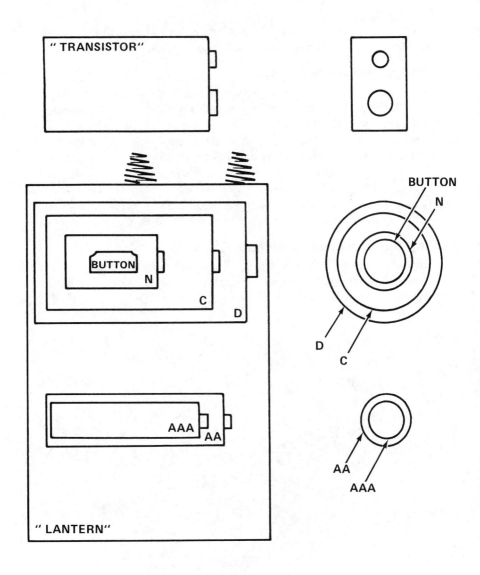

Figure 1-1.
Battery Shapes and Sizes

Batteries have a definite way in which they are inserted in equipment - a polarization. As you can see from Figure 1-1, many batteries have a slight bump that marks the *positive* pole (+) of the battery. The other end of such batteries is the *negative* pole (-). The 9-volt transistor battery has both poles on one end. Some batteries can be inserted the wrong way. If you buy new batteries and insert them and the equipment doesn't work, you may have to turn some or all of the batteries around. Most equipment now has a small diagram showing battery orientation.

How to Tell if a Battery is Low

Some battery-operated devices have a low battery indicator. The more important the application involved, the more likely the device will provide such an indication. For example, a battery-operated smoke detector may emit a chirping sound when its battery runs low. Other devices may have a low-battery light on their panel. In these cases, put your confidence in the equipment and remove and throw away the old batteries, or recharge them if they're ni-cads.

Other devices, such as radios or tape recorders, may not provide a low-battery indication. A low battery may mean you have to turn the volume up on a radio or recorder, or operation may become erratic or noisy.

Testing Batteries with a Battery Tester

The easiest way to test a battery is with a *battery tester*. Battery testers are small instruments about the size of a paperback book, as shown in Figure 1-2. They have a meter with a needle that swings to either a GOOD or REPLACE zone on the face of the meter.

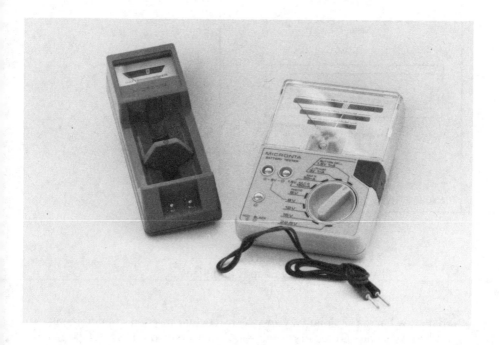

Figure 1-2.
Battery Testers

Testing a battery is easy. Remove the battery or batteries from the equipment, noting which way they were installed. Set the batteries just removed apart from any new batteries to avoid getting them mixed up.

Note the voltage on the battery case, as shown in Figure 1-3. Set the selector knob on the battery tester to the voltage of the battery. Sometimes there will be an additional selection for the type or size of battery, as for AAA or AA.

One type of battery tester has two leads coming from the unit, usually a red lead and a black lead. Press the tip of the red lead to the positive pole (+) of the battery and the tip of the black lead to the negative pole (-) of the battery. The needle of the battery tester should move to a zone. If the needle is in the GOOD zone, the battery is still good. If the needle is in the REPLACE zone, throw the battery away or recharge it in the case of ni-cads. If the needle is in between the good and the bad zone, you'll probably save yourself some trouble by replacing the battery with a new one to avoid further testing.

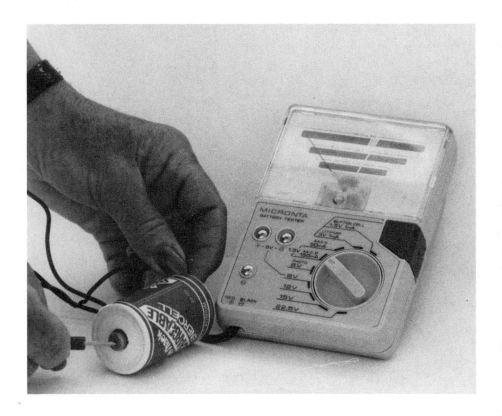

Figure 1-3.
Selecting the Battery Tester Voltage

If the meter needle doesn't move or tries to move "off scale", *reverse the leads* and try again.

Some battery testers have two special contacts for 9-volt transistor batteries. In this case, just select a 9-volt setting and set the transistor battery over the contacts to read the battery condition.

Some battery testers have a single negative pole contact. In this case, put the negative pole of the battery on the contact and use the red lead of the tester to probe the other pole, as shown in Figure 1-4.

Some battery testers have a special slot for "button" type batteries. In this case, select the type, insert the battery in the slot, and press down on the switch to test, as shown in Figure 1-5.

The smaller type of battery tester shown in Figure 1-2 doesn't even have a selector knob. You simply insert the battery in the proper opening, moving a bar

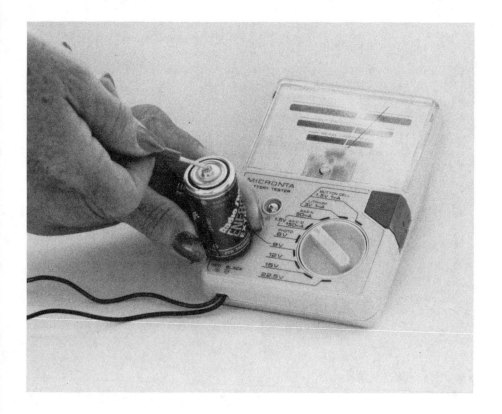

Figure 1-4.
Testing Batteries

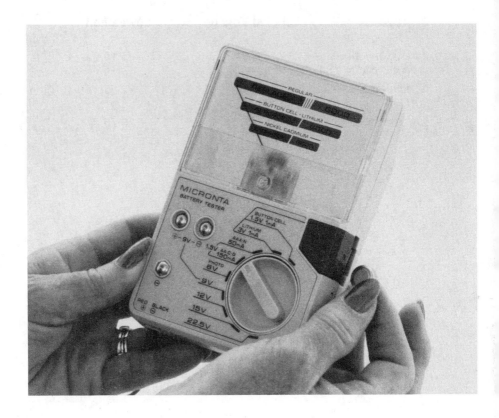

Figure 1-5.
Testing Button Batteries

down as you do so. The opening used selects the range of voltage settings in effect. The meter is read as before.

Testing Batteries with a Multitester

As most batteries start to lose their stored energy, their voltage drops. A battery may be tested with a *multitester*, a special electrical testing instrument described in Chapter 4. The voltages that designate batteries are often "rounded" to make even numbers and may be slightly lower or higher. Table 1-1 shows different types of batteries, their labeled voltages, and the lower limit of their voltage for reliable operation. Replace them if their voltage readings are below this value.

Type	Labeled Voltage	Lower limit
Button cell	1.5	1.15
AAA, AA, N, C, D	1.5	1.15
Lithium	3	2.25
Lantern	6	4.5
Transistor	9	6.75
12 volt	12	9
15 volt	15	11.25
22.5 volt	22.5	16.9

**Table 1-1.
Batteries and Voltage Limits**

Chapter 2
Continuity Testing of
Wires

Voltage and *current* were briefly described in Chapter 1. Voltage was compared to water pressure and current to water flowing through a hose. *Resistance* is another electrical quality. It takes longer to fill up a swimming pool with a 5/8-inch diameter garden hose than a 2-inch fire hose. The smaller-diameter garden hose has more *resistance* to the flow of water. The same thing holds true in electrical circuits. A smaller diameter wire has more electrical resistance to the flow of current than a larger one. More electrical energy burns off as heat in the smaller diameter wire. You can't easily feel this heat for the most part, but it's there.

In addition to wire size, different materials have more or less resistance. Glass, for example, has great resistance to electrical current, so much so that it's called an *insulator*. Gold has very little resistance, and makes a good *conductor*.

Voltage is measured in volts and current in amperes. Resistance is measured in *ohms*. The greater the value in ohms for a wire, the greater the electrical resistance and the less current that will flow.

Common Wiring

Wiring used for telephone lines, speakers, audio cables, television cables, outdoor low-voltage lighting, control wires for sprinkler valves, and security systems is *copper* wire. Copper is a very good conductor - not as good as gold, but much more practical.

Two types of copper wires are generally used: *solid* wire and *stranded* wire. Solid wire is one long continuous piece of copper material, as shown in Figure 2-1. Stranded wire is made up of individual strands of wire, twisted together in a bundle. Stranded wire should be used when the wire is subjected to bending - there's more "give" to the wire and it will not break as easily.

Wire sizes are calibrated in what is called the American Wire Gauge (AWG). When you hear someone talk of putting in "number 14 wire", they're talking about wire that is size 14 in the American Wire Gauge. In the AWG, the greater the diameter of the wire, the lower its AWG number, and the smaller the diameter of the wire, the greater its AWG number. Number 24 wire is small diameter wire used for security systems and low-voltage applications. Number 12 wire might be

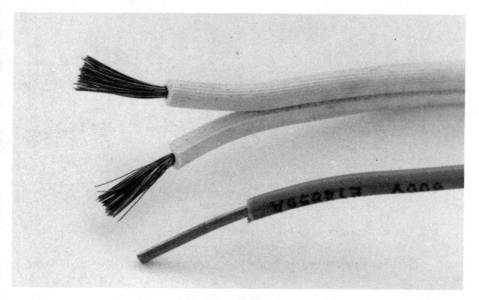

Figure 2-1.
Solid and Stranded Wire

used for household wiring. Number 4 wire is often used for car battery "booster" cables. Figure 2-2 shows the AWG sizes for common types of wiring.

SAFETY WARNING

In the following testing procedures, we're assuming that you will be testing for continuity of wires used in telephone lines, speakers, audio cables, television cables, outdoor low-voltage lighting, control wires for sprinkler valves, and security systems - *low-voltage* wiring. In this chapter we are not discussing testing continuity for *high-voltage* household wiring. See Chapter 5 for a description of those techniques.

Whenever testing any wires for continuity, make certain that the device used with the wires is unplugged from household wiring so that no electrical voltage exists on the wires. Also, be very careful in testing wires that are strung throughout a house or outside of a house. The wires should not come in contact with high-voltage household or exterior wiring. High-voltage electricity can easily KILL.

Continuity of Wires

Wires break when they are twisted around nails, subjected to continual bending, or just have normal use over a long period of time. Normally, copper wire has a resistance of 1 to 100 ohms per 1000 feet, depending upon the diameter and type of wire. This is virtually a "dead short". When wires are not continuous, or "open", their resistance is the resistance of air, hundreds of billions

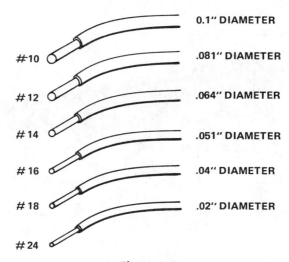

Figure 2-2.
American Wire Gauge

of ohms between two wires separated by 1/1000 of an inch. You can see, then, that even if wires appear to be touching, the wires have great resistance if there's any gap at all, and no electricity will flow.

Simple Continuity Tester

A simple $5 continuity tester is shown in Figure 2-3. It consists of a metal probe and indicator light powered by two AAA batteries. The probe is one lead of the continuity tester and can be touched to the end of a wire or inserted into a connector hole. The second lead is a clip lead that comes out of the body of the tester.

To use the continuity tester, insert the batteries and then touch the probe to the clip on the lead. The light should go on. (Always perform this preliminary step before using any continuity tester. It verifies that the continuity tester is working!) Now, connect the test lead to one end of the wire to be tested and the probe to the other end of the wire to be tested. If the wire is not broken, the light should come on.

Latching Continuity Tester

A latching continuity tester is shown in Figure 2-4. This tester is powered by a 9-volt battery inside the case and has an LED (light emitting diode) light as well as a buzzer. It has several different ways it operates.

Testing for Continuity

To test for continuity, set the switches to NORMALLY OPEN and MOMEN-TARY and then turn POWER ON. Now connect one test lead to one end of a wire

Figure 2-3.
Simple Continuity Tester

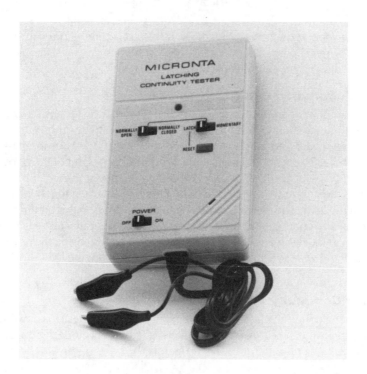

Figure 2-4.
Latching Continuity Tester

to be tested and the other test lead to the other end of the wire to be tested. The buzzer will sound and the LED light will go on if the wire has continuity.

Testing for Normally Open Circuits

Some circuits, in home security systems, are *normally* open. This means that switches are closed when a door or window opens or vibration (such as breaking glass) occurs. A typical circuit is shown in Figure 2-5. To test a circuit such as this, set the switches to NORMALLY OPEN and MOMENTARY and then turn POWER ON. Now connect one test lead to one end of a wire to be tested and the other test lead to the other end of the wire to be tested. The buzzer will not sound if the circuit is open. Closing any switch will cause the buzzer to sound.

Testing for Normally Closed Circuits

Also, some circuits, such as home security systems, are normally closed. This means that switches are opened when a door or window opens or vibration

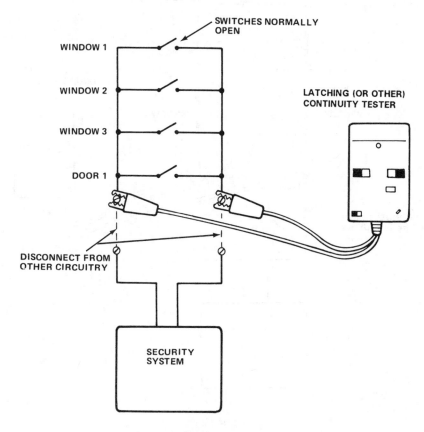

Figure 2-5.
Testing for Normally Open

occurs. A typical circuit is shown in Figure 2-6. To test a circuit such as this, set the switches to NORMALLY CLOSED and MOMENTARY and then turn POWER ON. Now connect one test lead to one end of a wire to be tested and the other test lead to the other end of the wire to be tested. The buzzer will not sound if the circuit is closed. Opening any switch will cause the buzzer to sound.

Testing for Intermittent Closures

Sometimes wires or circuits will be *intermittently* open. For example, jiggling or bending a wire may cause the wire to break open for a short time and then close again. The same thing may happen in reverse. When two wires are close together or switch contacts are very close, there may be no continuity until the wires are bent or stretched, at which time the wires or contacts may touch. There may even be cases where wires have continuity (or no continuity) until the temperature rises

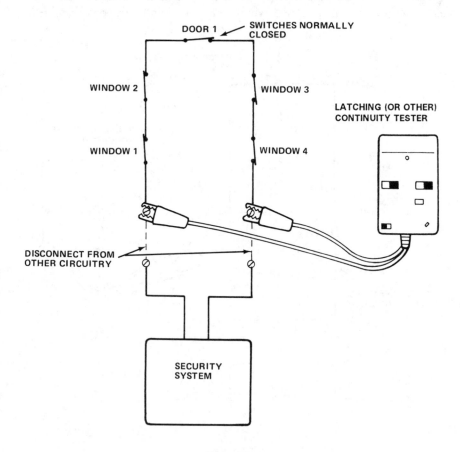

Figure 2-6.
Testing for Normally Closed

or falls to a certain level, at which time the wire opens or two wires touch as the material expands or contracts. A typical case is illustrated in Figure 2-7.

Such intermittent openings or closings are hard to find. A *latching* continuity tester makes them easier to find by detecting very short openings or closings. These might be so short that you would not hear the buzzer - a hundredth of second or less. The latching continuity tester detects these small openings or closings and then sounds the buzzer continuously until the tester is reset. You can even attach the continuity tester to a circuit overnight. If you return in the morning and the buzzer is on, an intermittent closing or opening occurred sometime overnight.

To detect intermittent closings, set the switches to NORMALLY OPEN and LATCH. Connect the test leads to the circuit. Press the reset button if the buzzer is sounding. The buzzer should now be silent but will sound if the circuit is closed for any brief period of time, or is permanently closed.

To detect intermittent openings, set the switches to NORMALLY CLOSED and LATCH. Connect the test leads to the circuit. Press the reset button if the

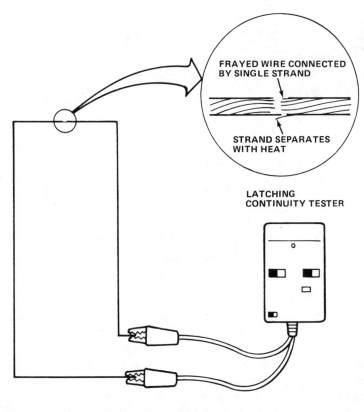

Figure 2-7.
Testing for Momentary Closures

buzzer is sounding. The buzzer should now be silent but will sound if the circuit is opened for any brief period of time, or is permanently closed.

Testing Audio System Connections

Audio Cables

Audio cables are generally *shielded* with a center conductor and shield of wire mesh on the outside, as shown in Figure 2-8. The resistance of such cables is very low, less than several ohms per 100 feet.

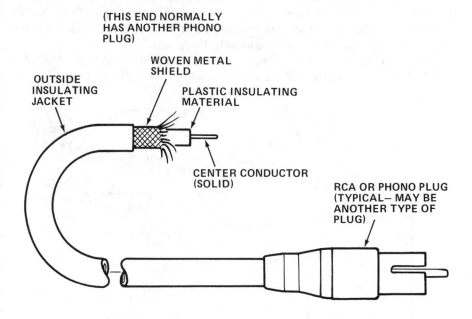

(THIS END NORMALLY
HAS ANOTHER PHONO
PLUG)

WOVEN METAL
SHIELD

OUTSIDE
INSULATING
JACKET

PLASTIC INSULATING
MATERIAL

CENTER CONDUCTOR
(SOLID)

RCA OR PHONO PLUG
(TYPICAL– MAY BE
ANOTHER TYPE OF
PLUG)

Figure 2-8.
Audio Cables

Often a continuity tester is not necessary to test audio cables. After all, you can hear sound through the system and it's obvious when the sound goes off or becomes noisy.

We'll assume that your system was working perfectly at one time and that it has recently developed problems. (See the Radio Shack book "How to Hook Up High-Tech Electronics" for information on new installations.) If you are playing records, tape cassettes, or CDs and have cables running from the player to an amplifier and are not getting sound, first look at the connections. Does jiggling the connector ends restore the sound? Does squeezing the cables over their length restore the sound? If so, you'll probably need to replace the cable - it has intermittent continuity. If you hear a great deal of hum in the system, the *shield* of the audio cable may be disconnected. In this case, also, replace the cable.

Before testing cables, unplug all equipment from the wall sockets. When testing audio cables, test both the center conductor and the outside shield conductor for continuity, as shown in Figure 2-9. If either conductor does not have continuity, replace the cable.

Speaker Connections

If one or more speakers do not work at one time, and did, first check to see if the speaker has a *fuse*. More expensive speakers may be fused to protect them from overload. If the speakers are not fused, you may have speaker wire that does not have continuity. Remove the speaker wires from the speaker end, but note carefully how the wires were connected. The wires may be of different colors. Label each wire so that you can reconnect them later. (The speaker *phasing* is affected if you switch the wires; the sound will be "muddy" in a stereo system.)

If the speakers are some distance from the amplifier or receiver, you may not be able to conveniently bring the cables back near the amplifier or receiver

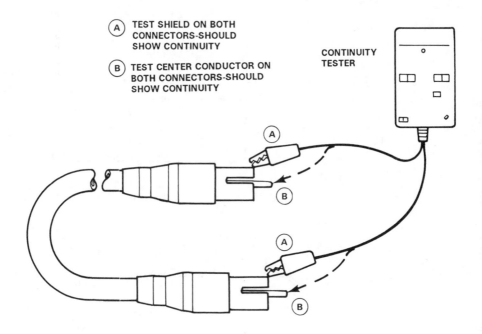

Figure 2-9.
Testing Audio Cables

connections. In this case, you may have to use a long wire to extend the continuity tester leads. The scheme is shown in Figure 2-10.

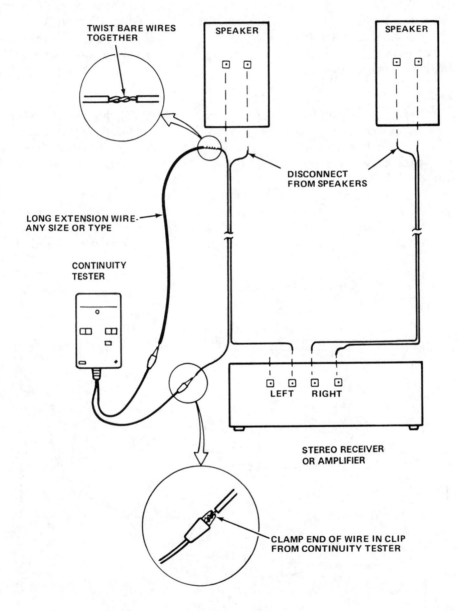

Figure 2-10.
Extending the Continuity Tester Leads

Testing Telephone Lines for Continuity

Phone lines are not complicated. Telephone cables consist of four to six separate conductors that are color coded, usually black, red, green, and yellow for the four-conductor case. Four-conductor cables are used for one or two phone lines and six-conductor cables for up to three lines. Phone connectors, such as those found at Radio Shack, have detailed instructions on how to connect the individual wires.

Often new homes are prewired for phone jacks. The builder is normally responsible for telephone wiring inside a new home, but you are responsible after any warranty period elapses. You are generally responsible for existing telephone wiring inside your older home as well. In any home or apartment you may be able to pay for a special service from your telephone company that enables you to call on them for repair.

New telephone lines may have breaks when lines are wrapped around nails inside walls. Even older lines may occasionally open up when there is a poor installation to begin with.

A telephone line is connected to the telephone system at an installation box in your home, as shown in Figure 2-11. Newer boxes have a plug which can be

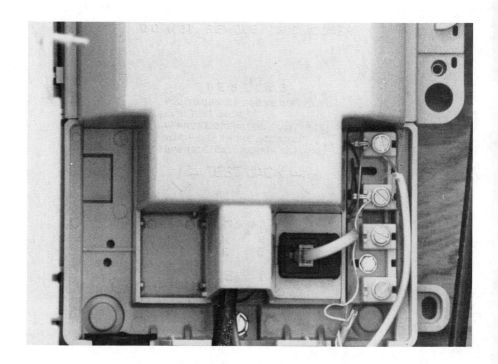

Figure 2-11.
Telephone Entry Box

disconnected to isolate your phone lines from the telephone system. If you can disconnect your phone line, you can use the continuity testers described above to test telephone lines.

If you cannot isolate your home telephone lines from the phone system by unplugging the lines at the entry box or by other means, DO NOT use continuity testers to test phone lines. The reason is this: When your local phone company rings your number, a *ringing voltage* of about 90 volts is sent through the line. If you should happen to be touching the line when this ringing voltage is sent, you might get an electrical shock, the voltage might cause a Pacemaker or other medical device to malfunction, or it may startle you and cause other problems. In extreme cases it could cause death.

A better way to test phone lines is by plugging a telephone into various jacks to see if it works. If there is no dial tone and the telephone works in another jack, the problem is in the continuity of the line.

Another approach is to use the Phone Tester shown in Figure 2-12. This tester plugs into a modular telephone jack and displays the condition of the line on two lights, a red and green LED. Some models will test two lines as well, each line being switch selective. If the green LED lights, the line is active and working. If the

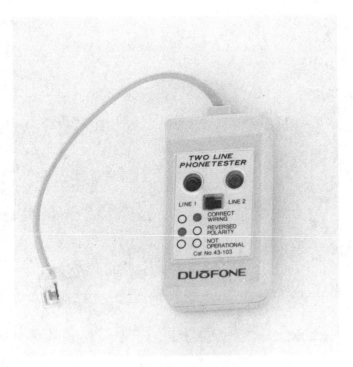

Figure 2-12.
Phone Tester

red LED lights, the line is active, but the two wires used for the telephone are reversed. If neither LED lights, the line has no continuity.

Testing Television Cables

Television cables, such as the ones from an outside or attic television antenna or cable television service, can also be tested for continuity. Like audio cables, television cables are shielded, with a center conductor and an outside wire mesh, as shown in Figure 2-13.

Television cables normally have removable connectors on each end, so they're easy to isolate from equipment. Disconnect all connectors before testing for continuity. Follow the procedures above for testing continuity of both the inner conductor and shield. Discard any cables that do not have continuity, if they are short enough. For longer cables, follow the procedure at the end of this chapter for finding the break.

Testing Low-Voltage Decorative Lighting and Sprinkler Systems

Low-voltage outdoor decorative lighting uses long runs of heavy (#12 to #16) wire to power lights similar to automobile headlights. Typical runs are one hundred feet for an average-sized city lot. Home sprinkler systems use valves that are controlled by a timer that sends a controlling voltage to turn the valves on.

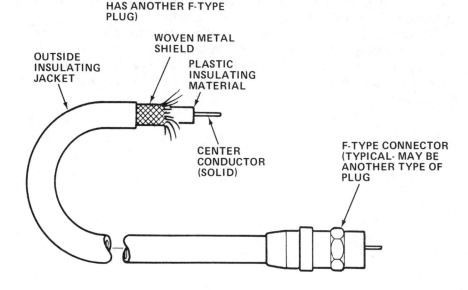

Figure 2-13.
Television Cable

Typical installations use runs of dozens of feet with #18 wire. A combination of continuity testing and voltage checking can be used to troubleshoot such systems. The procedures are described in Chapter 6.

Security Systems

There are several basic types of home security systems. One uses transmitters that plug into an ac power line and send signals to a master controller. Each room might have its own transmitter or two, connected to several windows or doors. The second type of security system uses a master controller with all signals sent via wire that is routed to individual rooms. Troubleshooting for the second type of installation is made very easy by the latching continuity tester, as it checks both normally open and normally closed circuits.

How to Repair Long Wires with Breaks

If you have a long wire with no continuity, a continuity tester will tell you that there *is* a break, but not *where* the break is. How do you find where the break has occurred? Here's one method: Find the a point halfway down the wire. Carefully stick a pin or needle into the wire as shown in Figure 2-14. Connect the end of the pin to a long lead from the continuity tester and check for continuity. Mark the spot and remove the pin. If there was continuity, take half of the final distance and do the same test again. If there was no continuity, take half of the distance up to the pin and repeat the test again. Using this "divide and conquer" approach you can find the one foot section in which the break is located in no more than seven tests of 100 feet of wire (50, 25, 13, 7, 4, 2, and 1 feet).

Once you have found this one foot section containing the break, verify it again by repeating the test before and after the break. Then cut the wire and splice in the appropriate connector. Connectors for the splice can be found for audio cable, television cable, security wiring, speaker wire, and other applications at Radio Shack.

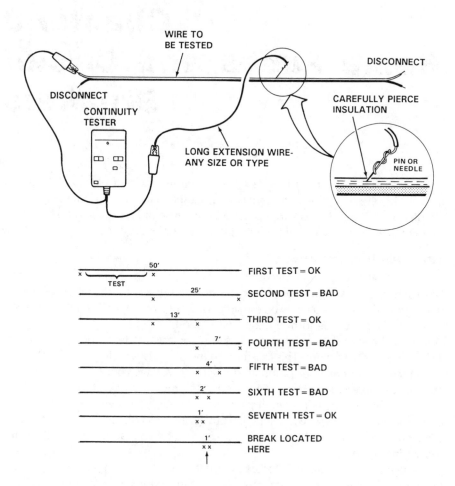

WIRE TO
BE TESTED

DISCONNECT

DISCONNECT

CONTINUITY
TESTER

CAREFULLY PIERCE
INSULATION

LONG EXTENSION WIRE-
ANY SIZE OR TYPE

PIN OR
NEEDLE

50′

TEST

FIRST TEST = OK

25′

SECOND TEST = BAD

13′

THIRD TEST = OK

7′

FOURTH TEST = BAD

4′

FIFTH TEST = BAD

2′

SIXTH TEST = BAD

1′

SEVENTH TEST = OK

1′

BREAK LOCATED
HERE

Figure 2-14.
Repairing Long Wires

Chapter 3
Home Fuses and Circuit Breakers

Home fuses or circuit breakers are the easiest type of electrical repair to make. However, a blown fuse may mask other electrical problems. In this chapter, we'll describe how to replace a blown fuse or reset a circuit breaker. In Chapter 5 we'll provide more information about home wiring.

The Main Power Panel

Electrical power comes into your home via two or three wires. The wires may be strung from power poles or may be buried underground. If the wires are buried underground, they are usually on the order of six feet down and do not pose much of a risk unless you perform a major excavation.

If you have two, rather than three, wires coming into your home, you have a 115-volt ac power system. This is usually found on houses built before 1940. Most appliances and consumer products run on this voltage, but certain models of appliances (dryers, for example) may operate only on 230 volts ac.

If you have three wires coming into your home, you have both 115 volts ac and 230 volts ac. Most of your electrical outlets are 115 volts ac, but you may have some outlets that supply 230 volts ac. Sockets for 115-volts ac and 230-volts ac are shown in Figure 3-1.

The main power panel is located close to where the main power lines come into your home. It's a large metal box as shown in Figure 3-2. Sometimes there are two metal boxes.

When the main lines come into your home they split off into several different *circuits*. A typical three or four-bedroom house might have 13 different circuits as follows:

Garbage disposal
Dishwasher
Other kitchen
Garage door opener
Air conditioner
Electric dryer
Washer
Ground fault interrupt (Bathrooms, etc.)

Lights and plugs 1
Lights and plugs 2
Lights and plugs 3
Lights and plugs 4
Lights and plugs 5

There are two good reasons for having different circuits. First, the electrical load is divided into branches that can use smaller diameter wire. If there was only one circuit, extremely heavy and expensive wire would have to be used to carry all of the current used by many appliances and electrical devices. Secondly, if there are several circuits, an overload in one circuit can be isolated without affecting other circuits. You may not want a freezer to be without power because of a shorted lamp cord, for example.

Figure 3-1.
Home Power Sockets

Figure 3-2.
Main Power Panel

Each circuit is protected from too much current by a *fuse* or *circuit* breaker. If there is a short, the fuse "blows" or the circuit breaker "trips", shutting off power to that circuit alone.

There is also usually a main fuse (or set of fuses) or circuit breaker that controls *all* power to the house. Four typical main power panels are shown in Figure 3-3.

Certain heavy-duty appliances may have their own smaller panel that has fuses or circuit breakers, as well. For example, an outside air conditioner may have a small power panel containing several fuses.

Fuses and circuit breakers both do the same thing. They break the circuit when there is a dangerous overload condition, shutting off all power in that circuit. If circuits were not fused or protected by circuit breakers, great amounts of current could flow. This would cause the wire carrying the current to heat up and possibly start a fire or melt the wire. At the very least, you'd have a huge electric bill if this current flowed continuously.

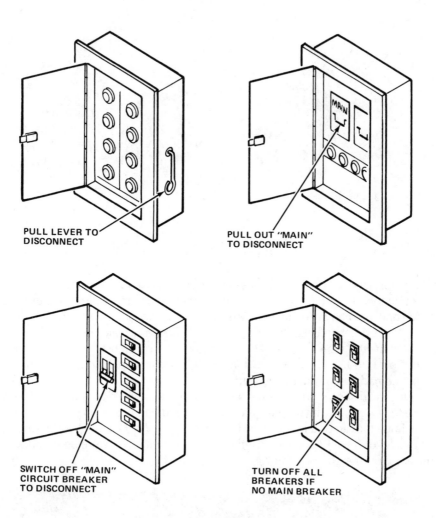

PULL LEVER TO
DISCONNECT

PULL OUT "MAIN"
TO DISCONNECT

SWITCH OFF "MAIN"
CIRCUIT BREAKER
TO DISCONNECT

TURN OFF ALL
BREAKERS IF
NO MAIN BREAKER

Figure 3-3.
Typical Main Power Panels

Fuses

There are three general types of fuses, as shown in Figure 3-4. The fuse on the left is an Edison base fuse. This is a screw in type fuse that is replaced like a light bulb. The fuse in the middle is a Type S fuse, a variation on the Edison base fuse. The fuse on the right is a cartridge fuse.

Screw Base Fuses

The Edison base and Type S fuses have a clear glass window that lets you see the fuse element. The fuse element is a strip of metal that melts when excessive

Figure 3-4.
Home Power Fuses

current flows in the circuit. Figure 3-5 shows both a good fuse and a "blown" fuse. If the window of the blown fuse is clear, chances are the fuse blew because you loaded one too many appliances on the same circuit and they were on at the same time. When this happens, the fuse element will heat up and melt.

If the blown fuse has a blackened window, there's a possibility that a "short circuit" occurred. This might mean that two wires in the circuit touched or that an appliance had a short that caused too much current to flow.

Often you can tell what caused the fuse to blow by what you did immediately before the fuse blew. If you plugged in a lamp and had everything else on at the same time - the radio, television, dishwasher, and iron - the circuit was probably just overloaded with appliances. If the fuse blew while you were doing nothing unusual, you may have a short in the circuit itself.

Figure 3-5.
Good Fuse Versus Blown Fuse

Time Delay Fuses

Time delay fuses look like other types of fuses but allow a little extra current to flow briefly when starting up appliances that use large motors. Appliances with motors cause a surge of current for an instant (less than a second) which might be enough to blow a normal fuse.

Cartridge Fuses

Cartridge fuses are cylinders that have the same general look, but vary in size. They do not have a window in which to see the element and must be *removed* and then tested with a continuity tester as described in Chapter 2 and shown in Figure 3-6. If there is continuity, the fuse is good.

Fuse Ratings

Circuits and fuses are rated in *amperes*, usually shortened to "amps". The higher the ampere rating, the more current that can be permitted to flow in the circuit. NEVER USE A FUSE OF HIGHER CURRENT RATING TO REPLACE A BLOWN FUSE. If you replace a 15-amp fuse, replace it with a 15-amp fuse. Replacing a fuse with one of higher current rating may cause a fire from excessive heat in wires.

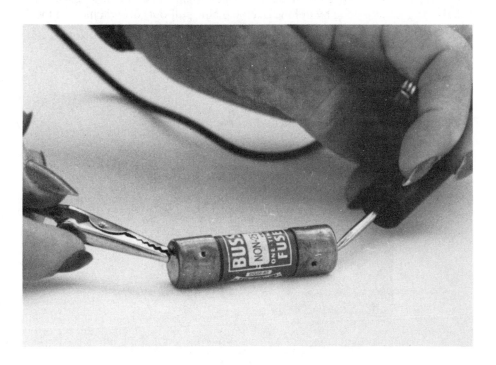

Figure 3-6.
Testing a Cartridge Fuse

Replacing Fuses

To replace a fuse, first try to determine the cause of the blown fuse. Remove all appliance plugs from the wall outlets and turn other appliances off except for necessary lighting. Next, locate the blown fuse by inspecting the fuses in the main power panel. When you have located the blown fuse, make certain you have a fuse of the same type for replacement.

Before replacing the fuse, observe these safety precautions:

• Make certain you are not standing in water, damp earth, or damp concrete.

• Wear shoes, preferably rubber soled.

• Handle the fuse by the edge, as shown in Figure 3-7.

• Use one hand when screwing in the fuse. Put the other in your pocket (this eliminates the possibility of you completing a live circuit through your upper body).

• Switch off the main power momentarily (make certain you have a flashlight if it is dark). This can be done by pulling out the main "pull-out" or switching off the main power switch, as shown in Figure 3-3.

Figure 3-7.
Handling a Fuse

Let's stress that this is not a dangerous operation if you observe these common sense safety precautions; however treat home wiring with respect at all times! After replacing the fuse, plug in the main "pull-out" or turn on the main switch. The fuse should not blow again. If it does, you may need the help of an electrician.

Circuit Breakers

Circuit breakers are a better method of protecting circuits. They are a type of switch that trips when too much current flows in a circuit. Before resetting a circuit breaker, first try to determine the cause of the circuit breaker trip. Remove all appliance plugs from the wall outlets and turn other appliances off except for necessary lighting. Next, locate the tripped circuit breaker by inspecting the breakers in the main power panel. When you have located the tripped breaker, move the switch to the ON position and release it. The circuit breaker should remain in the ON position after it is released. If it does not, you may need the help of an electrician.

Replacing the Main Fuses

In some cases, one or more main fuses will blow as well as a circuit fuse. These are usually cartridge fuses. Again, first try to determine the reason for the failure and disconnect or turn off as many electrical devices as possible. Then pull out the main pull-out and replace both cartridge fuses with fuses of the same rating. Save the ones replaced for later continuity testing by the method shown in Figure 3-6.

Chapter 4
Multitester Use

A *multitester* is a basic test instrument that measures direct current voltage, alternating current voltage, current, and resistance. It can be used for many different types of electrical testing - as a continuity tester, to measure household voltage levels at wall plugs, to test for high resistance that indicates bad cables, to measure low-voltage outdoor lighting currents and voltages, and to test switches, to mention a few applications. Another name for a multitester is a multimeter or voltohmmeter.

Types of Multitesters

There are two basic types of multitesters and they are shown in Figure 4-1. On the left is an analog type; on the right is a digital readout type. Both types measure the same things - they just display the results in different ways. The analog type has a needle on a dial that moves to various values. The digital type reads out directly in an LCD display like a digital watch.

Multitesters range in price from about $15 to $200 or more. Even the least expensive units perform the same basic functions as the most expensive. Each type has test leads that connect to plugs on the unit. One test lead is red and connects to the positive (+) jack. The other test lead is black and connects to the negative (-) jack. In addition to the test leads, multitesters have a rotary switch that selects the basic function - direct current voltage, alternating current voltage, current, and resistance.

Measuring Direct Current Voltage

The most basic measurement a multitester can measure is direct current voltage. For example, a multitester can measure the voltage of a battery, as shown in Figure 4-2. An *autoranging* multitester such as the digital readout unit shown selects the proper range of voltages automatically. An analog multitester requires that the rotary switch be set to the voltage range. Typical ranges are up to 1000 volts dc, up to 500 volts dc, up to 125 volts dc, up to 25 volts dc, and up to 5 volts dc.

As described before in this book, voltage is a measure of electrical "pressure". It's like water pressure in a hose. The higher the voltage of a battery or power supply, the more current that will be supplied for a given load, just as higher water pressure forces more water through a hose.

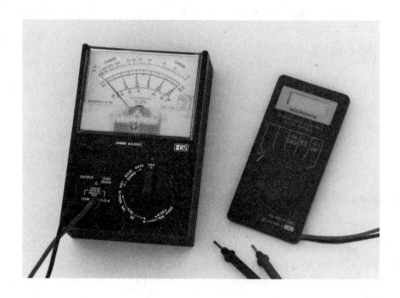

Figure 4-1.
Two Types of Multitesters

Figure 4-2.
Measuring Battery Voltage

33

Direct current flows in only one direction only. Batteries supply direct current, as do most power supplies.

Measuring voltage is done by selecting the direct current voltage function on the rotary switch of the multitester. Choose the highest range if the dc voltage is unknown. For the autoranging multitester, select the DCV setting.

After switching the multitester to DC volts, touch the red probe (+) to the positive pole of the battery or power supply and the black probe (-) to the negative pole of the battery or power supply. The digital readout multitester will display a value such as 9.51. The analog multitester will display a value on the DC scale of the meter, as shown in Figure 4.3. The mirror behind the needle is used to "line up" the needle for precise readings.

Measuring Alternating Current Voltage

WARNING

Never touch the metal part of the probes when measuring voltages with a multitester. Always grip the plastic portion of the probe. Do not stand in water or on a damp floor and wear rubber soled shoes if possible. Try to keep one hand in your pocket!

Alternating current electricity is generated by power companies. It travels from the generating plant (coal, hydroelectric, or nuclear) over high-voltage electrical lines. At various points, the high-voltage lines (typically 12,000 volts) feed other lines which reduce the high voltage to a lower voltage by *transformers*. These lines carry the electricity to other parts of the area and feed additional lines at an even lower voltage. At the end of this chain, the high voltage from the generating plant has been reduced to 230 volts ac which is connected to individual homes and businesses. Homes and businesses use either the 230 volts ac or sometimes only half of that voltage - 115 volts ac.

Alternating current electricity is basically the same as direct current, but reverses direction 60 times per second. This enables ac electricity to be reduced (or increased) by transformers. Transformers plugged into home wall sockets provide *low-voltage* power for outside landscaping lights, control of lawn sprinkler valves, and other applications. Small power supplies used with calculators, some computers, and telephones convert the 115 volts ac from wall sockets to direct voltage power, at 6 to 16 volts dc.

Since alternating current reverses direction 60 times per second it can't be measured in the same fashion as direct current. The multitester ACV switch selects special circuits inside the multitester to *rectify* the ac and convert it to dc so it can be read on the meter.

The ACV settings on the analog multitester and the ACV setting on the autoranging digital multitester allow ac voltages of up to 1000 volts to be read. To read an ac voltage, set the selector knob to the highest ACV voltage value. Then put either the red or black probe across any ac voltage point and the other lead across the other voltage point, as shown in Figure 4-4. Read the voltage from the

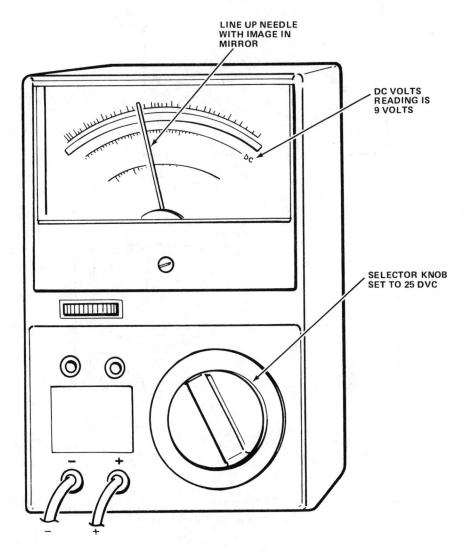

Figure 4-3.
Analog Scale Reading for Voltage

AC scale on the analog multitester or from the digital readout. Set the selector knob to lower values to get a more precise reading.

Measuring Direct Current

You can also measure *direct* current with most multitesters (not in the digital multitester pictured above, however). This function is not as useful as other multitester functions, though. Never use this function to measure ac current - it

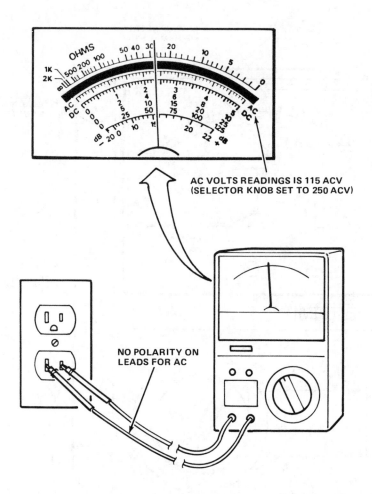

AC VOLTS READINGS IS 115 ACV
(SELECTOR KNOB SET TO 250 ACV)

NO POLARITY ON
LEADS FOR AC

Figure 4-4.
Reading AC Voltage with a Multitester

may damage the multitester. Figure 4-5 shows an example of measuring current from a battery to a light bulb. The procedure is the same for measuring current with other devices. First set the selector to DCA 250m. This setting will measure currents of up to 250 milliamps. A milliamp is 1/1000 amp, so currents of up to 250/1000 amp or 1/4 amp can be measured.

Now put the red lead on the positive pole of the battery and the black lead on one terminal of the light bulb. The connection from the negative pole of the battery goes to the other light bulb terminal. Read the current from the DC scale. Typical currents to flashlight bulbs are 40 to 600 milliamps. (The 250 milliamp range may not be great enough to measure high currents.)

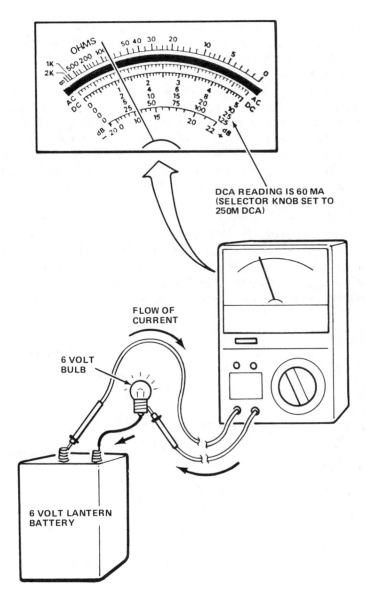

DCA READING IS 60 MA
(SELECTOR KNOB SET TO
250M DCA)

FLOW OF
CURRENT

6 VOLT
BULB

6 VOLT LANTERN
BATTERY

Figure 4-5.
Measuring Current with a Multitester

Measuring Resistance

As mentioned in Chapter 2, the resistance of a wire impedes the flow of current, much like using a garden hose to fill a swimming pool rather than a fire hose. The garden hose has more resistance. The greater the diameter of wire, the less the resistance. The better conductor used in a wire, the less the resistance - gold is a slightly better conductor than copper and copper is a much better conductor than pencil lead.

The R scale on a multitester is selected to measure resistance. In the digital autoranging multitester, the selector switch is set to KΩ, which stands for kilo ohms or thousands of ohms. In the analog multitester the settings are Rx1, Rx10, or Rx1K, standing for ohms, tens of ohms, or thousands of ohms.

Wire has very low resistance, typically less than an ohm per hundred feet, so the Rx1 or Rx10 scale is probably the most useful scale for home and automotive applications. (There are devices used in electronics that provide standard resistance values of fractions of ohms to millions of ohms. The Rx1K scale is useful for troubleshooting these devices, but their use is beyond the scope of this book.)

Measuring resistance by a multitester is somewhat different than measuring voltage. Never use the resistance measurement with the wire or part to be measured connected in the circuit. Always remove it from the source of power.

For the digital multitester, follow this procedure: Connect the leads of the multitester to the wire or part to be measured, as shown in Figure 4-6. Either lead

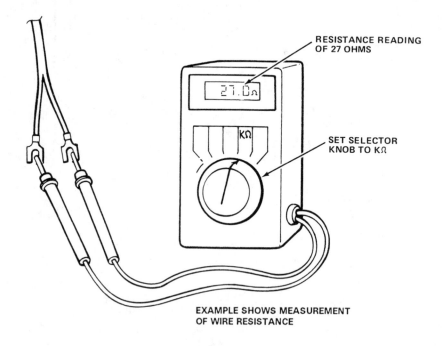

RESISTANCE READING
OF 27 OHMS

SET SELECTOR
KNOB TO KΩ

EXAMPLE SHOWS MEASUREMENT
OF WIRE RESISTANCE

Figure 4-6.
Reading Resistance with a Digital Multimeter

may be connected to either end - there is no positive or negative side. Read off the resistance measurement in XX.X ohms on the digital readout. Note the tiny Ω mark in the lower right corner of the display. It indicates ohms. This may change to KΩ for higher resistance values. If the resistance is greater than the capability of the digital multitester, you'll see a blinking 1 in a display of 1000 KΩ. This means "open", or at least a resistance greater than 2,000,000 ohms.

For the analog multitester, follow this procedure. Select Rx1 for measuring the resistance of a wire. Now touch the two probes together firmly. While holding the leads together, adjust the OHMS ADJUST knob until the needle reads exactly 0 on the OHMS scale of the meter (the needle should swing over to the right). Now select Rx1, Rx10, or Rx1K. Connect the leads of the multitester to the wire or part to be measured, as shown in Figure 4-7. Either lead may be connected to either

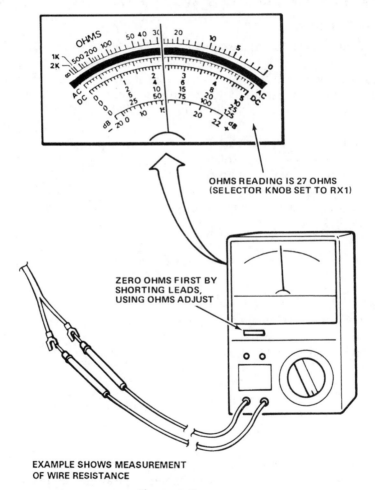

OHMS READING IS 27 OHMS
(SELECTOR KNOB SET TO RX1)

ZERO OHMS FIRST BY
SHORTING LEADS,
USING OHMS ADJUST

EXAMPLE SHOWS MEASUREMENT
OF WIRE RESISTANCE

Figure 4-7.
Reading Resistance with an Analog Multimeter

end - there is no positive or negative side. Read off the resistance measurement on the OHMS scale. If you've selected Rx1, this will be the actual resistance in ohms. If you've selected Rx10, multiply the reading by 10. If you've selected Rx1K, multiply the reading by 1000. The reading in the figure is 27 ohms.

If resistance readings are higher than a few ohms for wire connections, you may have a bad connection. For example, a reading of 200 ohms for a 100 foot run of outdoor low-voltage lighting wire is not acceptable. Similarly, there should be an "open" between two wires in the same cable that are not connected. A resistance reading of a few thousand ohms is not acceptable.

An Advanced Topic

There are two rules that are handy to know when working with household repair. The first of these is *Ohm's Law*. The second is a way to calculate power.

Ohm's Law

Ohm's Law tells you the current if you know the resistance and voltage, the voltage if you know the current and resistance, and the resistance if you know the current and voltage. Current is in amperes, voltage is in volts, and resistance is in ohms. Ohm's Law relates to direct current but can be extended for alternating current as well. Here are the three forms of Ohm's Law:

    current = voltage/resistance
    voltage = current x resistance
    resistance = voltage/current

If a 6-volt flashlight bulb has a resistance of 50 ohms, then the current flowing through it is:

    current = 6/50 amperes = 120/1000 amperes = 120 milliamperes

Power

The other rule is more useful in home and automotive applications. It tells you power if you know the voltage and current, voltage if you know the current and power, and current if you know the voltage and power. Voltage is in volts, current in amperes, and power in watts.

    power = voltage x current
    voltage = power/current
    current = power/voltage

For example, suppose you have an iron rated at 1150 watts that plugs into a wall socket. How much current will it require? The average current when the iron is on (it cycles on and off) will be current = 1150/115 = 10 amps

Suppose that you have ten 12.5 watt low-voltage lighting bulbs that require 16 volts ac. How much current is required?

Since the bulbs are connected across the wire, each requires

current = 12.5/16 = .8 amps
The ten bulbs require 10 x .8 amps = 8 amps.

How much power can a 20 ampere circuit in home wiring provide?

power = 115 x 20 = 2300 watts

This power would be consumed by a television (300 watts), a microwave (800 watts), an iron (1150 watts), and a 50-watt bulb, if they are running at the same time (the iron and microwave may cycle on and off).

Chapter 5
Testing Home Wiring

Installing home wiring is a job for an electrician or a very competent do-it-yourselfer. However, there are many simple tests that you can make to your home wiring to save expensive repair bills. Most of these tests will require very little in the form of equipment.

However, before you even think about testing, please note that household electricity can KILL. You must always be careful of the dangers posed by home wiring and observe these simple rules:

• NEVER work on a live circuit. Always turn off the circuit breaker or pull the fuse to that circuit and verify that the power is off.

• Always try to handle electrical wires by the insulated part and avoid touching the bare wire.

• Wear dry shoes with rubber soles and heavy socks.

• Never stand in water while working on electrical circuits, Avoid damp basement floors and damp ground whenever possible.

• Always be extremely careful when in the vicinity of high tension wires. NEVER get near the wires with ladders, poles, or wires of any type.

• Remember that even low-voltage circuits may cause a slight shock under the right circumstances, or may cause a spark. The shock or spark may startle you and cause other accidents, such as slips or bruises.

• When testing outlets or circuits, NEVER handle testing devices by their probes or bare leads. Always hold them by their plastic or insulated parts.

Fuses and Circuit Breakers

Read Chapter 3 to find out about the fuses and circuit breakers in your home, where they are located, and how they operate.

Testing Two-Wire Outlets

Older electrical outlets have two holes into which you insert a two-pronged plug, as shown in Figure 5-1. To test for electrical power from such outlets, use a neon light electrical tester, as shown in Figure 5-2. This tester will test any circuit from about 80 to 500 volts. The tester consists of two leads which connect to a neon light. The leads do not have *polarity* - you can switch leads during testing with no effect.

Being careful not to touch the exposed pins, insert the two leads from the tester into the two holes of the receptacle. The neon lamp should glow. If it glows,

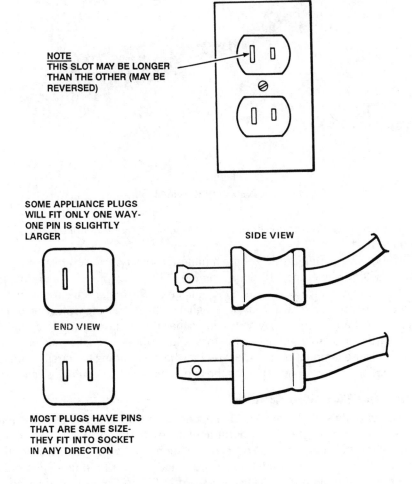

Figure 5-1.
Two-Wire Outlets

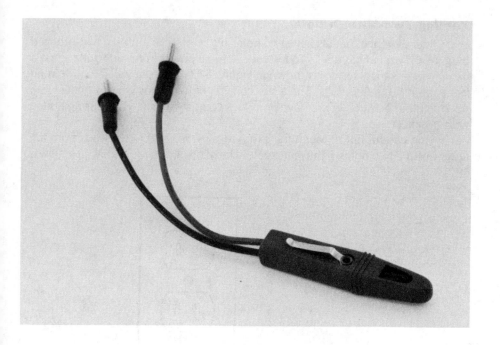

Figure 5-2.
Neon Light Tester

the circuit is on or "hot" and should provide power to an appliance plugged into the outlet.

If you have a multitester: Set the multitester selection switch to an ACV (ac voltage) setting higher than 100 (for example, 250). Now plug the leads into the outlet as shown in Figure 5-3. Read the voltage on the meter scale for an analog multitester or on the digital display for a digital multitester. If the voltage reading is much lower than 115, you may have wire in the circuit with too small a diameter, reducing the available voltage. This may show up as a smaller picture on a television, for example. In this case, you may be overloading the circuit with too many appliances or may need to have the wiring replaced. Consult an electrician.

Grounding Two-Wire Outlets

Newer outlets use three wires and appear as shown in Figure 5-4. The third hole is for a grounding pin. Many home appliances, tools, and machines now use a three-wire grounding plug. You can use such a plug in a two-wire outlet, providing that your metal outlet box is grounded. To test for a grounded outlet box, connect the neon tester leads as shown in Figure 5-5. If the outlet box is grounded, the lamp will glow. You can now use a ground adapter plug to convert the outlet into a three-wire grounded outlet as shown in Figure 5-6.

Figure 5-3.
Reading AC Voltage with Multitester

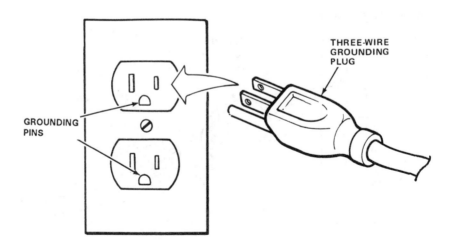

Figure 5-4.
Three-Wire Outlet

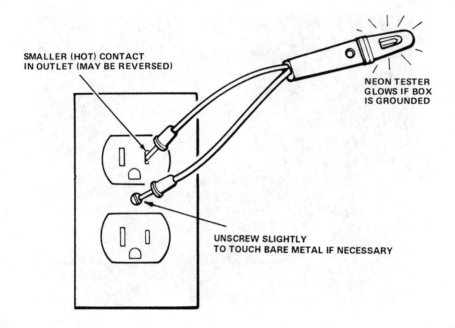

Figure 5-5.
Testing for Grounded Box

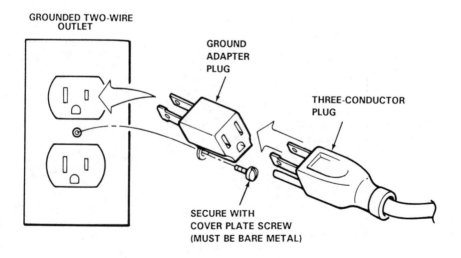

Figure 5-6.
Ground Adapter Plug

Why Grounding Is Important

A grounded outlet is important because appliances and tools are not perfect. Wires may fray or become loose. When this happens, a live wire may contact the metal case of the appliance or tool. If this case is grounded, current will flow from the live wire to the ground wire causing a "short". This will blow a fuse or trip a circuit breaker in your main electrical box, removing electrical power from that outlet and all other outlets on the circuit. If the case is not grounded and you touch the case with one hand and household plumbing with your other hand, current will flow through you and give you an electrical shock. Under the wrong circumstances, such a shock can kill you.

Many appliances and tools that are used in kitchens, bathrooms, in the basement, outside, or near water have three-wire grounded plugs. These plugs should be connected to ground either through a three-wire adapter or to a three-wire outlet. If you are using such tools in a two-wire ungrounded plug, it may be best for your safety to have the outlet grounded by an electrician.

If your outlet is grounded but uses a two-wire outlet, you may want to convert it to a three-wire plug yourself, as described later in this chapter.

Testing Three-Wire Outlets

Newer outlets have three holes as shown in Figure 5-4. The bottom hole is a ground contact. You can test these outlets to see that they are properly grounded and "hot" by using an ac circuit analyzer, shown in Figure 5-7.

Ac circuit analyzers have three indicator lights, as shown in Figure 5-8. These indicator lights indicate the state of the outlet. CHECK YOUR OWN INDICATOR LIGHT INSTRUCTIONS TO SEE THE MEANING OF THE LIGHTS. Figure 5-8 shows the typical meanings of different light combinations.

If the outlet is wired properly, the "Correct" indication will appear on the lights. In a typical tester, this is the case in which the two lights on the right (often green) light. If another combination of lights illuminate, the outlet is improperly wired. Refer to "Replacing an Outlet" later in this chapter.

To test the voltage with a multitester: Set the multitester selection switch to an ACV (ac voltage) setting higher than 100 (for example, 250). Now plug the leads into the outlet as shown in Figure 5-3. Read the voltage on the meter scale for an analog type or on the digital display for a digital type of multitester. If the voltage reading is much lower than 115, you may have wire in the circuit with too small a diameter, reducing the available voltage. This may show up as a smaller picture on a television, for example. In this case, you may be overloading the circuit with too many appliances or may need to have the wiring replaced. Consult an electrician.

Turning Off Power at an Outlet

While working on electrical circuits, you must first turn off electrical power to the outlet by turning off the main electrical power, by removing a fuse for the circuit, or by throwing the proper circuit breaker to the off position. To find the

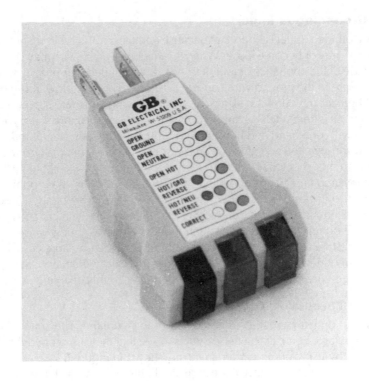

Figure 5-7.
AC Circuit Analyzer

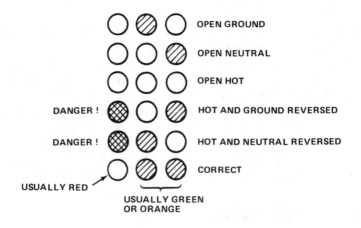

Figure 5-8.
AC Circuit Analyzer Light Codes

proper fuse or circuit breaker, follow this procedure: Plug a lamp or radio into the outlet. Turn the lamp or radio on. Find the main circuit box and look for a label identifying the circuit. If you cannot find such a label (often there is none or it's too difficult to decode), turn off the circuit breakers or remove the fuses one by one until the lamp goes out or the radio turns off. Now insert the fuse or turn on the circuit breaker again and verify that the lamp or radio goes on again. Now turn off the circuit breaker or remove the fuse again and verify again that the lamp or radio goes off. Repeat the procedure for all outlets in the box. Leave all fuses out or circuit breakers off that control any outlet in the box. Make certain that no one else can come near the main circuit box and turn the power on by mistake while you are working on the circuit, or attach a warning sign - something like "Danger - Do Not Touch - Working on Circuits!".

While you are working on a circuit, make certain it stays dead. If you are turning the power on and off, make certain that you don't turn the power on and leave it on when you come back to finish work on the circuit!

Things to Look for When an Outlet is Dead

Blown Fuses or Tripped Circuit Breakers

The most obvious thing to look for when an outlet is dead is a blown fuse or tripped circuit breaker. Read Chapter 3 to find out how to change a fuse or reset a circuit breaker.

Ground Fault Circuit Interrupt

Another thing to check is whether the outlet is in a *ground fault circuit interrupt*. A ground fault circuit interrupt (also called a GFI or GFCI) is a circuit that is used for outlets used in bathrooms, kitchens, garages, basements, and outdoor locations. These locations are potentially dangerous places because of the possible shocks from faulty electrical devices used around water or dampness. A ground fault interrupt is very sensitive and will rapidly shut off power before most people will suffer injury.

There are two types of ground fault interrupt outlets. One type is used for a single outlet. The second type is used for many outlets on the same circuit. Both types may look the same. Both types have a built-in circuit breaker, as shown in Figure 5-9. The type that handles many outlets in the same circuit may be located in the garage or basement. Before resetting the circuit breaker in the GFI, try to locate what may be causing the ground fault. An electrical appliance in a swimming pool, a faulty bathroom appliance, or a short circuit in outdoor lighting are all examples of conditions which would trip a ground fault circuit interrupt breaker. Reset the GFI circuit breaker by pressing down on the RESET button on the GFI. If the GFI circuit breaker trips again, look harder at the possible cause.

Outlet Controlled by Switch

Another possible cause of a dead outlet occurs when one of the outlets in a dual outlet is dead and the other is live. The dead outlet may be controlled by a

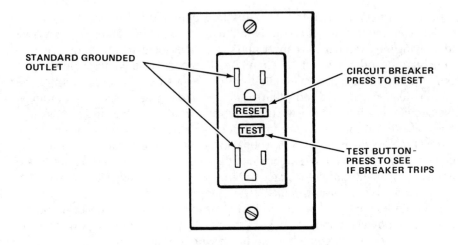

Figure 5-9.
GFCI Outlet and Circuit Breaker

wall switch which has mistakenly been switched off. Try turning on some of the wall switches in the same room as the dead outlet to see if that solves the problem.

Connecting Wires

Note

The majority of homes use copper wire. Some older homes have *aluminum* rather than copper wire. Aluminum wire has a silver color; copper wire has a reddish color. Aluminum wire requires special fittings. Do not connect switches, outlets, or other electrical devices to aluminum wire unless they are marked with the letters *CO/ALR* or *AL/CU*. Failure to do so may cause overheating and a fire.

Screw Terminals

When connecting a wire to screw terminals, form a C shape with the wire. Then put the wire under the head of the screw and around the screw in the *same direction* as the screw is tightened, as shown in Figure 5-10. This keeps the wire tight to the screw and under the screw head.

Wire Nuts

Many wires in electrical boxes are connected by *wire nuts*. Wire nuts are shown in Figure 5-11. To connect two or three wires with wire nuts, twist the wires around each other and then insert into the wire nut. Now twist the wire nut completely around two or three times. If the wires are properly connected, they will not be loose in the wire nut and will not pull out when given a slight tug. Make certain that the wire nut is large enough to accommodate all wires - wire nuts come in a variety of sizes and colors.

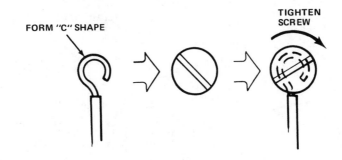

Figure 5-10.
Attaching Wire to Screw Terminals

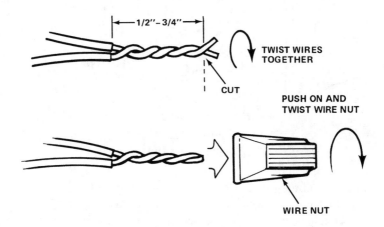

Figure 5-11.
Wire Nut Use

Replacing Outlets

When fuses or circuit breakers are all right, when all other outlets in your house work, and when there is no GFI circuit at the outlet or somewhere else, then you probably have a bad outlet. Replacing an outlet is not too difficult, but remember to observe the safety rules at the beginning of this chapter.

To replace an outlet, follow these instructions (see Figure 5-12):

1. Test the outlet for power using the circuit tester and turn off the circuit breaker, main switch, or fuse so that *both* or *all* outlets are dead. See "Turning Off Power at an Outlet".

2. Remove the outlet cover plate. Usually this requires removing only a single screw.

3. Remove the top and bottom screws holding the outlet to the electrical box.

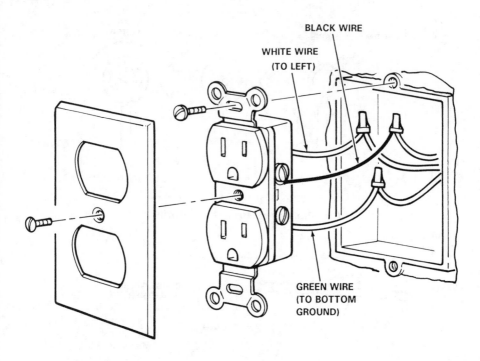

BLACK WIRE

WHITE WIRE
(TO LEFT)

GREEN WIRE
(TO BOTTOM
GROUND)

Figure 5-12.
Replacing an Outlet

4. Carefully pull the outlet from the electrical box.

5. Note which wires go to which screws or holes in the outlet. There are two general types of outlets, those with wires wrapped around screw connections and those with wires pushed through holes in the rear of the outlet (the latter type usually has screw terminals as well). Draw a simple diagram to help you remember the color and placement of the wires. (See Figure 5-13.)

6. Depending upon the type of outlet (two or three wire) you will probably see white, black, and green wires. Green or bare wires are ground wires that connect to a grounding screw on the outlet. Some two-wire outlets will not have a grounding wire. Generally, black (hot) wires go to the right contacts and white (neutral) wires go to the left wires.

7. Disconnect the wires from the outlet. This means you will have to unscrew the wires from screw terminal outlets or release the wires from the other type. The quick release type of outlet releases the wires if you push a small slot screwdriver into a release hole.

8. Check a possible link between the upper and lower outlet. If the link is broken (see Figure 5-14) you must break the link in the same place on a replacement outlet. To break the link, bend it back and forth several times.

9. Reconnect the wires in the same position for the new outlet.

10. Push the outlet back into the electrical box and reconnect the outlet with the top and bottom screws.

11. Replace the cover plate.

12. Turn on the power and test the circuit, preferably with an ac circuit analyzer to verify proper connections.

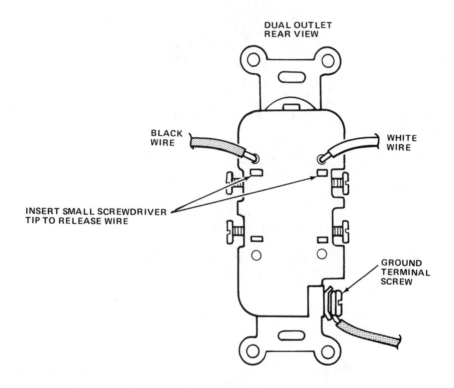

Figure 5-13.
Wires on Outlet

Testing Switch Circuits

There are two general types of switch arrangements: a single-pole switch controlling a light or outlet or a two-switch circuit in which a light or outlet is controlled by two "three-way" switches. The two-switch case is often found in hallway lights where there is a switch at one end of the hallway and a second switch at the other end of a hallway. (There are also circuits that control a light or outlet from more than two switches, but they are not common.)

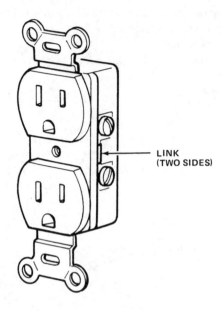

LINK
(TWO SIDES)

Figure 5-14.
Link on Outlet

In either case, if a switch fails to operate a light or turn on power to an outlet, check the obvious possibilities first:

• If a light is involved, is the light bulb bad?

• Is the fuse blown or circuit breaker tripped for the light or outlet circuit?

• Is the light or outlet in a ground fault circuit interrupt and has the GFI circuit breaker been tripped? (See "Ground Fault Circuit Interrupt" above.)

Testing a Single-Pole Switch

Test a single-pole switch circuit as follows:

1. You must turn off the power for the circuit in which the switch and light (or switch-controlled outlet) is located. If the switch is not functioning, this is difficult to test. IF YOU DO NOT KNOW FOR CERTAIN WHICH CIRCUIT IS INVOLVED, TURN OFF ALL POWER! Another way of determining the circuit is to leave the power on and remove the switch cover plate. Without removing the actual switch, you may be able to see screw terminals on the switch. If so, use a circuit tester as shown in Figure 5-15. Connect one lead to the switch box (ground) and the other lead to each of the switch terminals that have a wire connected. The neon light may light for one of these terminals. If so, turn off the circuit breaker or remove the

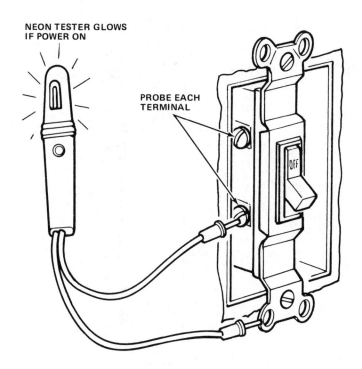

NEON TESTER GLOWS
IF POWER ON

PROBE EACH
TERMINAL

Figure 5-15.
Testing Switch Power in the Circuit

fuse so that power is removed from the terminal. If the circuit tester does not light on either terminal, turn off ALL power. See "Turning Off Power at an Outlet".

2. Remove the outlet cover plate. Usually this requires removing only a single screw.

3. Remove the top and bottom screws holding the switch to the electrical box.

4. Carefully pull the switch from the electrical box.

5. Note which wires go to which screws or holes in the switch. There are two general types of switches, those with screw terminals and those that use wires pushed through holes in the rear of the outlet (the latter type usually has screw terminals as well). Draw a simple diagram to help you remember the color and placement of the wires. (See Figure 5-16).

6. Disconnect the wires from the switch. This means you will have to unscrew the wires from screw terminal outlets or release the wires from the other type. The quick release type of outlet releases the wires if you push a small slot screwdriver into a release hole.

7. You now will have the switch completely removed from the circuit with no wires attached. You can now test the switch by using a continuity tester or

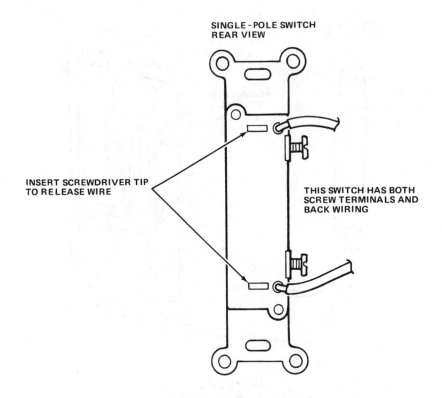

SINGLE-POLE SWITCH
REAR VIEW

INSERT SCREWDRIVER TIP
TO RELEASE WIRE

THIS SWITCH HAS BOTH
SCREW TERMINALS AND
BACK WIRING

Figure 5-16.
Wires on Single-Pole Switches

multitester. Attach one lead of the continuity tester to one screw terminal or a piece of wire pushed into a push-in terminal. Probe the other screw terminal with the continuity tester probe. See Figure 5-17. Operate the switch. The continuity tester should show continuity when the switch is in the ON position and no continuity when the switch is in the OFF position. There should be no continuity between the mounting bracket of the switch and either terminal. If the switch is good there is a problem somewhere else in the circuit - call an electrician.

8. Reconnect the wires in the same position for the new switch (or old switch if found to be good).

9. Push the switch back into the electrical box and reconnect the switch with the top and bottom screws.

10. Replace the cover plate.

11. Turn on the power and test the circuit.

Testing a Two-Switch Circuit

Test a two switch circuit (one that uses "three-way" switches) as follows:

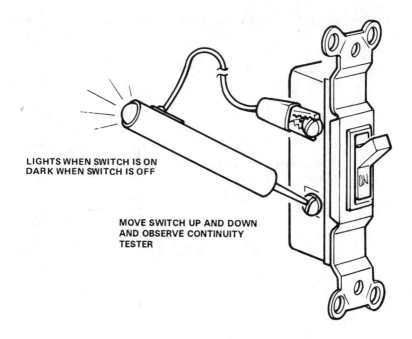

LIGHTS WHEN SWITCH IS ON
DARK WHEN SWITCH IS OFF

MOVE SWITCH UP AND DOWN
AND OBSERVE CONTINUITY
TESTER

Figure 5-17.
Testing a Switch Out of the Circuit

1. Follow the steps above to remove the suspected switch. Make certain that power is off at both switches, if necessary by turning off all power.

2. Test each switch in turn unless one switch operates the light or outlet and the other does not.

3. When you have one of the two switches completely removed, with no wires connected, test the switches as follows: You can test a switch by using a continuity tester or multitester. Attach one lead of the continuity tester to the screw terminal marked COM or COMMON. Probe one of the other two screw terminals with the continuity tester probe. See Figure 5-18. Operate the switch. The continuity tester should show continuity when the switch is in one position but not the other. Now probe the second screw terminal. The continuity tester should show continuity when the switch is in one position but not the other. The continuity should be opposite for each screw terminal - when one is on the other should be off. There should be no continuity between the mounting bracket and any terminal.

4. If the switch tests good, there is a problem somewhere else in the circuit. May be best to call an electrician.

5. Reconnect the wires in the same position for the new switch (or old switch if found to be good).

6. Push the switch back into the electrical box and reconnect the switch with the top and bottom screws.

7. Replace the cover plate.

8. Turn on the power and test the circuit.

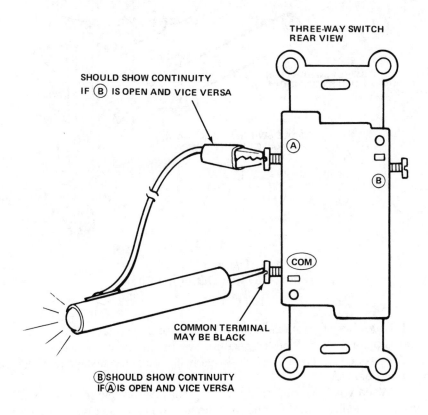

THREE-WAY SWITCH
REAR VIEW

SHOULD SHOW CONTINUITY
IF (B) IS OPEN AND VICE VERSA

COMMON TERMINAL
MAY BE BLACK

(B)SHOULD SHOW CONTINUITY
IF(A)IS OPEN AND VICE VERSA

Figure 5-18.
Testing a Switch From a Two-Switch Circuit

Chapter 6
Testing Low-Voltage
Circuits

In this chapter we'll look at common household low-voltage circuits. These are circuits such as doorbells, sprinkler controls, decorative outdoor lighting, and the like that use reduced voltages to power the devices. Because the voltage is much less than the 115 volts ac found in home electrical outlets, working with such circuits is usually not as dangerous as with the ac circuits discussed in the last chapter.

Transformers

A *transformer* converts 115 volts ac into a lower voltage, typically 10 to 24 volts ac. Examples are doorbell transformers, transformers used for heater controls (thermostat), and transformers used for outdoor decorative lighting. A typical doorbell transformer is shown in Figure 6-1.

A typical transformer connects to 115 volts ac in a "junction box" using wire nuts, as shown in Figure 6-2. Usually there are two wires that go the white and black wires of the electrical circuit. There may also be a third ground wire, usually green, that connects to the frame of the transformer. The transformer is usually "on" all the time - there is no switch connected to it.

Another type of transformer plugs into an ac wall socket with a grounded two- or three-connector plug, as shown in Figure 6-3. Small versions of this transformer operate calculators, tape recorders, small televisions, and many other household devices.

The wires coming *in* to the transformer must be handled with extreme care. These are 115 volts ac and can give you a severe electrical shock or KILL you. Observe all safety rules shown in Chapter 5 when dealing with these wires.

The wires coming out of the transformer, or the screw terminal contacts found on a transformer, provide low-voltage "safe" power to operate door bell chimes, thermostats, low-voltage lights, or other household devices. Although these wires usually cannot shock you, they still must be handled with care. Shorting the wires (touching them together) will usually blow a fuse in the circuit to which the transformer is connected or even heat the wires to temperatures that melt the wires. Shorting them may cause a spark as well, startling you and causing you to injure yourself in some other way.

Figure 6-1.
Typical Doorbell Transformer

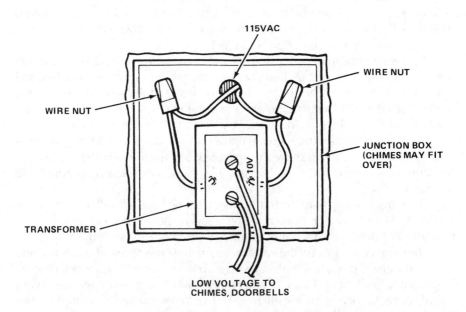

Figure 6-2.
Transformer Connections

Figure 6-3.
Small Appliance Transformer

Doorbell Circuits

Doorbell circuits usually operate with transformer voltages of 10 to 24 volts ac. A typical doorbell circuit has a transformer, doorbell chime, front door doorbell, and rear door doorbell, as shown in Figure 6-4.

Although the chime connections vary, there may be a screw terminal connection for one lead from the transformer and two other screw terminals, one connected to the front doorbell and the other connected to the rear doorbell, as shown in the figure.

If your doorbell does not work, the most likely cause is a bad doorbell switch, especially if one doorbell works and the other does not. Other problems might be a break in the wire leading to the front or rear doorbell, a bad chime unit, or a bad transformer.

To test the doorbell, try to remove the doorbell switch from the wall. Once the switch is removed, take any piece of wire and short the two contacts together, as shown in Figure 6-5. If the doorbell sounds, the switch is bad and you'll have to replace it. If the doorbell still does not sound, the doorbell switch is good, but you may have a broken wire, bad chimes, or a bad transformer.

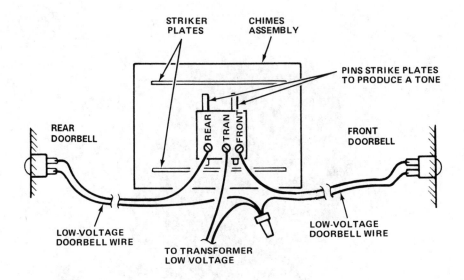

Figure 6-4.
Typical Doorbell Circuit

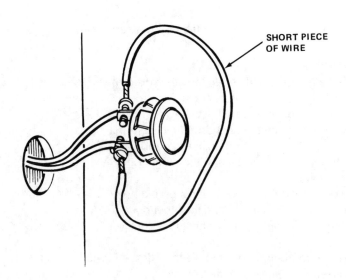

Figure 6-5.
Testing a Doorbell Switch

Test the transformer by using a multitester across the output (NOT INPUT) terminals, as shown in Figure 6-6. Set the multitester to ACV (ac voltage) greater than 24 volts. The voltage should measure the voltage marked on the transformer, usually 10 to 24 volts. If the voltage does measure this amount, the doorbell transformer is good. If the voltage is 0, the transformer may be bad, or the input leads (115 volts ac) may be broken or disconnected.

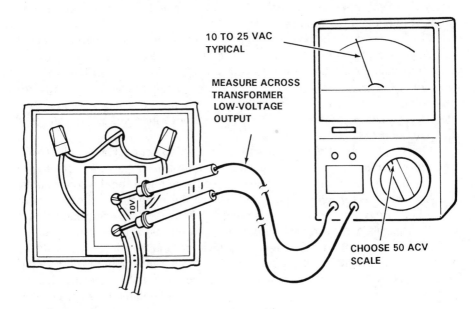

Figure 6-6.
Testing a Doorbell Transformer

If the doorbell switch is good and the transformer is good, the other causes are broken wires leading from the transformer to the chimes or switch or a bad chimes unit. If there are two circuits in the chimes unit, try reversing the front and back door wires. If the chimes now work for the doorbell, the problem is in the doorbell chimes unit. If the doorbell still does not work, reverse the wires again - the problem is in the wiring to the doorbell.

If the problem is in the chimes unit, try cleaning the strikers that hit the chime - they are pulled up or down by the electrical current in a coil. Move them back and forth to free them. If this does not work, you may have to replace the entire chimes unit.

Sprinkler Controls

There are many different sprinkler controls, ranging from commercial units to small household units. We'll describe a simple household unit, costing less than

$100. The main sprinkler control is a box about the size of a thick book. This mounts on the wall and is connected by a grounded three-wire connector to a wall outlet in a garage or basement. Newer units may connect to a small transformer that plugs into a wall socket and supplies low-voltage power to the box. Be very careful when testing this unit to stay away from the 115-volt ac side of the unit. Usually this is not a problem as the box is insulated and high voltage parts are not exposed. NEVER open the box and try to repair the unit internally - you may be exposed to dangerous voltages.

On the outside of the box are four to nine screw terminals. These connect to electrically-operated sprinkler valves, as shown in Figure 6-7. Inside the box (or at the wall outlet) is a transformer that converts 115 volts ac into low voltage, typically 24 volts ac. The control unit energizes the proper valve at a predetermined time to turn on the sprinkler. Each sprinkler valve has two wires; they are not polarized - there is no positive or negative wire here, as the voltage is alternating current.

One of the screw terminals is usually marked "COM" or "COMMON". This is a common terminal that goes to one wire of each sprinkler valve. The other wire from each sprinkler valve goes to one of the other terminals on the control unit.

If no sprinklers are working, the problem may be in the main sprinkler control box. There are two types of timing and control in these units - mechanical and digital. The mechanical control units trip a switch as a dial - really a clock movement - rotates around. The switch is tripped on and then off, or two switches are tripped. The digital controls use a small computer internally to energize the outputs. Either control is complicated and you must follow the instructions provided with the unit. Make certain that you have programmed the unit correctly. Most units have the ability to energize the outputs manually to test the sprinklers or to water. Try this to see if all outputs are functioning.

If the control box has a fuse, as shown in Figure 6-8, unscrew it and examine the fuse to see if it has blown (use a continuity tester if unsure). If the fuse is blown, you may have a short in one of the sprinkler outputs. Replace the fuse and then disconnect all outputs, replacing them one at a time and testing them to make certain there are no shorts. If the fuse blows again, you will have the problem isolated to a single sprinkler valve and can then look for a shorted circuit there. Disconnect the line and use the continuity tests described in Chapter 2.

If one or more sprinklers are not working, use a multitester to see if an ac voltage appears on each output in turn. If so, the problem is not in the control unit and must be in either the wiring or the sprinkler valve.

If one or more sprinklers are still not working, measure the voltage at the sprinkler valve in manual mode, as shown in Figure 6-9. The voltage should be nearly the same as in the control unit, although it may be somewhat lower due to the length of the wire. If there is 0 volts at the sprinkler value, the problem is in an open wire. Disconnect the wire at the control unit and then test for continuity using the procedures in Chapter 2.

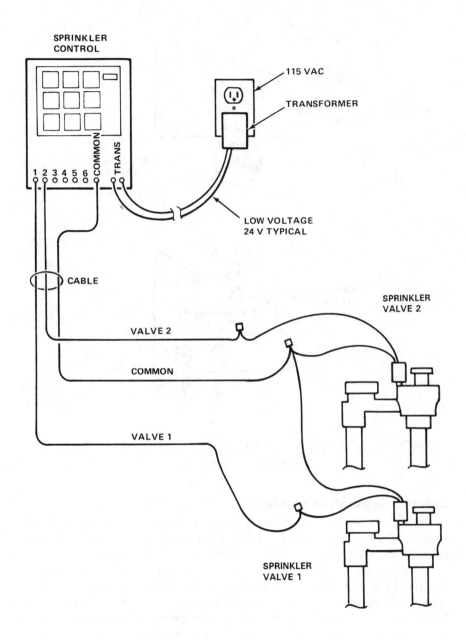

SPRINKLER
CONTROL

115 VAC

TRANSFORMER

COMMON
TRANS

1 2 3 4 5 6

LOW VOLTAGE
24 V TYPICAL

CABLE

VALVE 2

COMMON

VALVE 1

SPRINKLER
VALVE 2

SPRINKLER
VALVE 1

Figure 6-7.
Typical Automatic Sprinkler Connections

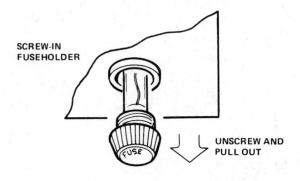

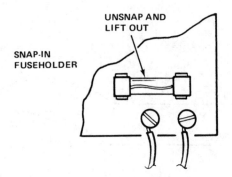

Figure 6-8.
Fuse on Control Box

Exterior Decorative Lighting

Again, there are many different outside lighting systems. We'll describe a simple household unit, costing less than $100 and supplying six to 12 lights. The main lighting control unit is a box about the size of a small toolbox. This mounts on the wall and is connected by a grounded three-wire connector to a wall outlet in a garage, basement, or outside location. Be very careful when testing this unit to stay away from the 115-volt ac side of the unit. Usually this is not a problem as the box is insulated and high voltage parts are not exposed. NEVER open the box and try to repair the unit internally - you may be exposed to dangerous voltages.

On the outside of the box are two screw terminals. These connect to heavy waterproof wire, usually 12 to 16 gauge. This wire is meant to be buried in the ground if necessary. Inside the box is a transformer that converts 115 volts ac into low voltage, typically 12 volts ac. The control unit terminals are not polarized - there is no positive or negative terminal here, as the voltage is alternating current.

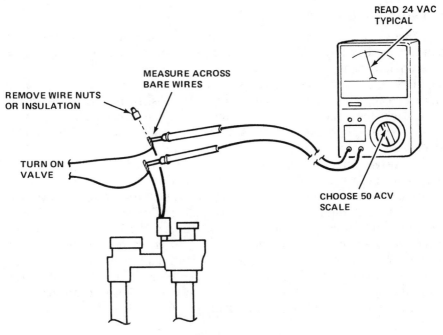

READ 24 VAC
TYPICAL

MEASURE ACROSS
BARE WIRES

REMOVE WIRE NUTS
OR INSULATION

TURN ON
VALVE

CHOOSE 50 ACV
SCALE

Figure 6-9.
Measuring the Voltage at the Sprinkler Valve

The control unit is usually a mechanical rotating dial which is essentially a clock movement. The dial trips a switch as it rotates around. The switch is tripped on and then off, or two swithes are tripped. Make certain that you have programmed the unit correctly and that the device is truly on. Most units have the ability to energize the outputs manually to test the lights. Try this to see if any lights come on.

If any lights come on, the problem is not in the control box, as the lights are fed power in parallel - in this case current is getting through the wire, at least initially. If no lights come on, see if the control box has a fuse, as shown in Figure 6-8. Unscrew or unsnap the fuse to see if it has blown. If so, you may have a short in the wire supplying the lights. In this case, replace the fuse and disconnect the wire. Then follow the procedure for finding shorts given in Chapter 2.

If the fuse has not blown, replace it and use a multitester to see if an ac voltage appears on the output terminals. If the proper voltage appears - about 12 volts - the problem is not in the control unit and must be in the wiring to the lights. In this case, use the multitester to check each light in turn measuring the ac voltage at each light. It should be 2/3rd or greater of the voltage at the control box terminals. The wire is often strung as one long circuit, so if the light at the end of the circuit is on, you'll know that the problem must be at the connection to individual lights that do not light. Reseat the connections to each light, being careful to avoid shorting the wires. Most lights have a set of contacts which pierce the two wires when a cover is screwed or pressed tight, as shown in Figure 6-10.

Power Supplies

There's another type of device that plugs into a wall socket that is like a transformer. It's a low-voltage *power supply* that powers calculators, some computer equipment, tape recorders, and the like. The power supply is used to convert the 115 volts ac to direct current very similar to what you get from a battery. Direct current voltage values are typically 6 volts to 16 volts. These devices are usually marked with the name "Class 2 Transformer" or the like even though they provide direct current. The input (115 volts ac) and output voltages are also usually marked on the case.

These types of power supplies are reliable, but may fail. You can test them by using a multitester set to DCV and putting the probes across the plug from the device, as shown in Figure 6-11. The plugs vary, but a typical plug is shown. The plug is *polarized* - one side is positive and the other negative, so put the red lead of the multitester on the center connector of the plug and the black lead of the multitester on the outside connector of the plug when testing. The device should read the full voltage or more than the full voltage marked on the outside of the case. If you read 0 volts dc or a very low value, the device is probably bad. You can find a replacement from Radio Shack, but when you do, be certain to get one that has the same output voltage and same output current capacity.

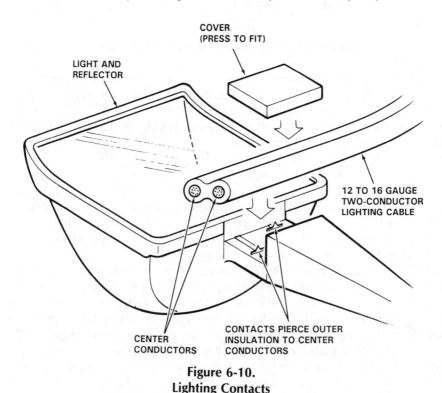

Figure 6-10.
Lighting Contacts

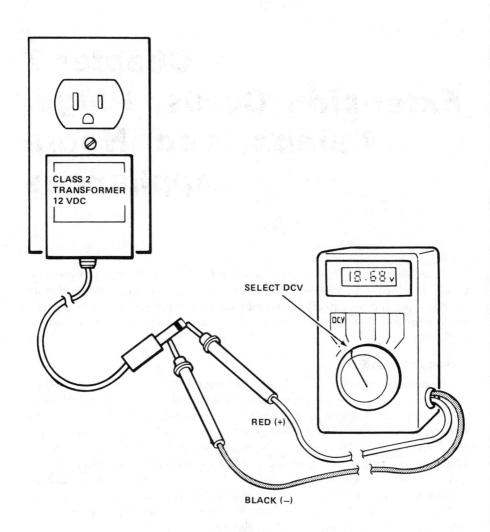

CLASS 2
TRANSFORMER
12 VDC

SELECT DCV

DCV

RED (+)

BLACK (−)

Figure 6-11.
Testing Power Supplies

Chapter 7
Extension Cords, Plugs, Lamps, and Home Appliances

Extension cords, lamps, and fluorescent lights can be easily tested and repaired by the do-it-yourselfer. Home appliances have become more and more sophisticated and usually are beyond the ability of most consumers (and many repair people!). However, we can provide a few tips on problems with these as well in this chapter.

Extension Cords

Extension cords are simple devices that extend electrical power safely when not misused. You should never overload an extension cord with many appliances that require a great deal of power. If you do, the extension cord may become too hot and could actually cause a fire. For the same reason, it's not good to put extension cords under rugs or in furniture. Another safety rule: use three-conductor extension cords (with a ground) when appropriate, for example, in a garage, basement, kitchen, or bathroom. The ground connection on such an extension cord protects you by providing a ground on an appliance or tool, making certain that a fuse or circuit breaker is blown in case of a shorted wire. The alternative is electrical shock or even electrocution.

To test an extension cord, use a continuity tester as described in Chapter 2 and shown in Figure 7-1. All terminals on one end of the extension cord should match the terminals on the other end of the extension cord and should show continuity (note that the two power connections are reversed between the two connectors!). You should also use the continuity tester to test for intermittent continuity in case there are breaks in the cord that become apparent only when the cord is twisted or stretched.

Look at the ends of extension cords to see if the wires to the plug are split or frayed. If so, throw away the cord, or put on a new plug.

Putting a New Plug on a Cord

To put a new plug on an extension cord or appliance follow these directions.

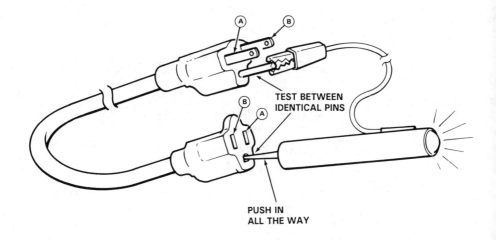

TEST BETWEEN
IDENTICAL PINS

PUSH IN
ALL THE WAY

Figure 7-1.
Testing an Extension Cord for Continuity

Two-Wire Plug

A light-duty two-wire plug such as those found for small lamps, radios, and small televisions can be replaced by two-conductor press-to-connect plugs, shown in Figure 7-2. (There are many types; the one shown is common.) Such a plug can be used for two-conductor "square" wire, but not for round wire. Cut the wire squarely. Make certain that no individual strands are present that might short out. Slide the wire through the hole in the shell of the plug. Spread the prongs of the body of the plug apart and slide the wire into the rear of the body so the two wires are separated from each other. Press down on the prongs and push the body into the shell. This action pierces each wire with a barbed contact. Test the connection by plugging in the light or device and trying it. If the device doesn't work, open up the plug and observe how the contacts pierce the wire. It might be necessary to move the wires slightly for a better contact.

Two-Wire Plug for Larger Cable

There is no press-to-connect plug for heavier electrical cord. Two-wire round or heavier square cable is usually used for larger appliances that do not require a grounded plug. The replacement plug is usually a little larger then the original molded plug. It has two screw terminals under which the wire is fastened, as shown in Figure 7-3.

Cut the cord away from the old plug. Thread the cord through the rear of the plug. Put an "Underwriter's knot" (see Figure 7-4) in the cord and then strip off about 1 1/2 inches of the outer insulation from the cord if necessary (there is no outer insulation with heavier square cord). The best way to strip off the insulation is with a wire strippers, but you can also do it with a scissors or wire cutters if you are very careful not to cut the two wires underneath the covering.

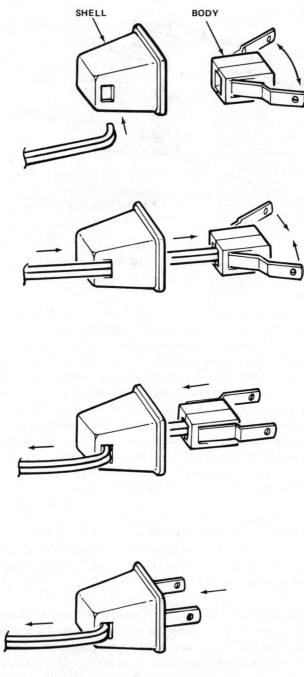

Figure 7-2.
Installing a Press-to-Connect Plug

Figure 7-3.
Two-Wire Plugs

Separate the two wires and cut off any fabric material between the wires. Now strip about 5/8 inches of insulation from the ends of each of the two wires. Twirl the strands of each of the three wires between your fingers to make one solid core. Form each wire into a "C" shape and put it under the screw in the same direction that the screw will be tightened. Tighten the screw, making certain that the wire is under the screw head and that no individual strands of wire stick out to possibly short out the plug. Repeat for the second wire.

Three-Wire Plug

Three-wire grounded plugs are usually used for heavier appliances that require a grounded plug for safety reasons. For example, three-wire grounded plugs are used for appliances and products that are used in kitchens, bathrooms, basements, garages, and outdoors. Don't try to defeat the purpose of these plugs by replacing them with anything other than a three-wire grounded plug, examples of which are shown in Figure 7-5. Such plugs are usually more bulky and may not look as attractive as the original molded plugs, but are safe.

The three wires in such electrical cords are usually white, black, and green. The green wire is ground. Cut the cord and push through the rear of the plug. Strip off about 1 1/2 inches of the outer insulation from the cord, as shown in Figure 7-6. The best way to strip off the insulation is with a wire strippers, but you can also do this with a scissors or wire cutters if you are very careful not to cut the three wires underneath the covering.

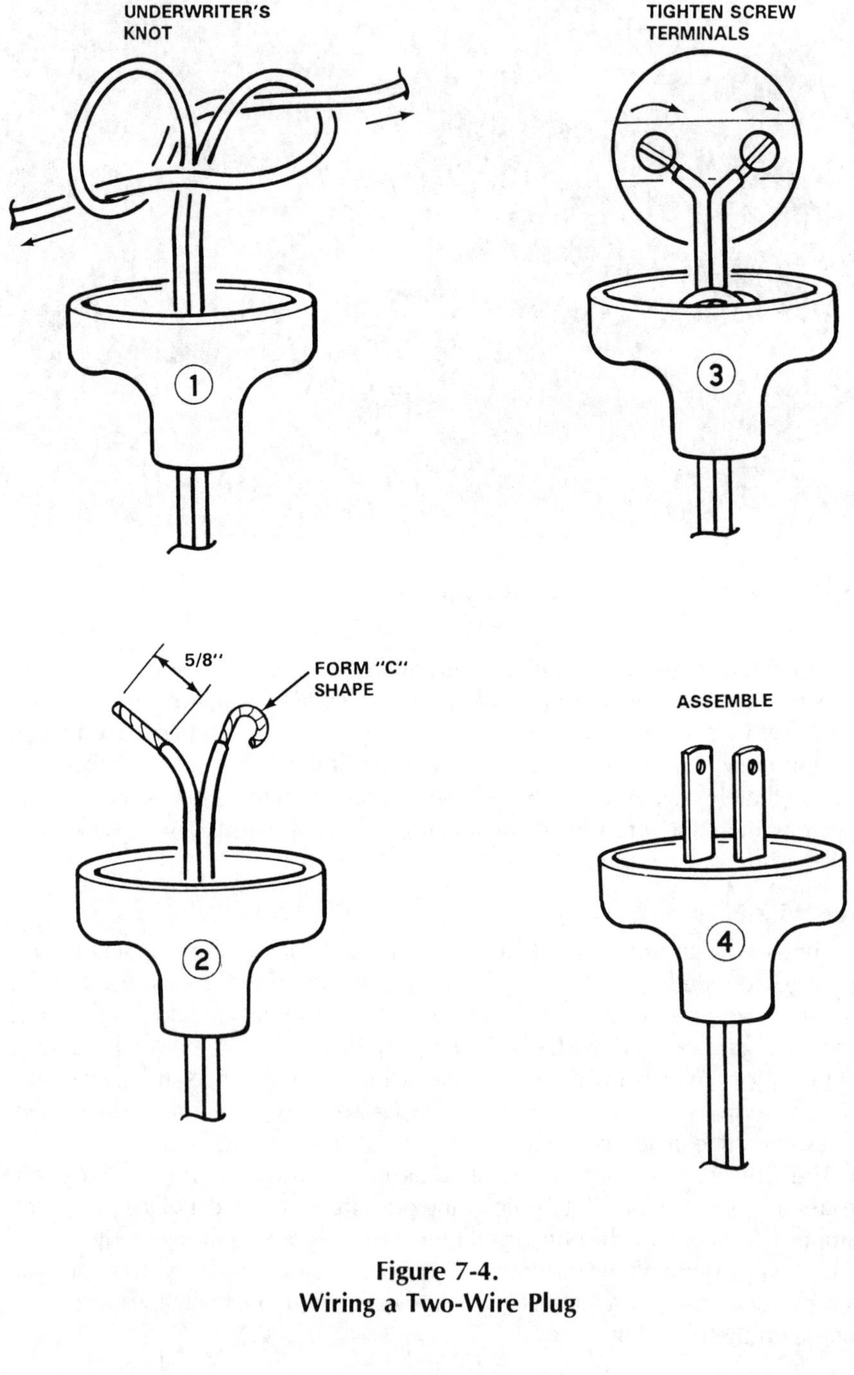

UNDERWRITER'S
KNOT

TIGHTEN SCREW
TERMINALS

① ③

5/8''   FORM "C"
SHAPE

ASSEMBLE

② ④

Figure 7-4.
Wiring a Two-Wire Plug

Figure 7-5.
Three-Wire Plug

Separate the three wires and cut off any fabric material between the wires. Now strip about 5/8 inches of insulation from the ends of each of the three wires. Twirl the strands of each of the three wires between your fingers to make one solid core. Form the ground wire into a "C" shape and put it under the ground screw in the same direction that the screw will be tightened. Tighten the screw making certain that the wire is under the screw head and that no individual strands of wire stick out to possibly short out the plug. Connect the other two wires in the same fashion. Tighten the screws on the two straps at the rear of the plug against the wire. This strap provides "strain relief" so that a pull on the cord does not pull out (and possibly short) the wires from under the screw terminals.

Testing Lamps

Lamps are simple devices. They plug into a wall outlet, usually with a two-conductor plug. The two wires from the plug go through the lamp body and are then are routed to a socket/switch combination, as shown in Figure 7-7. In some cases another type of switch may be used and one of the wires may first go to this switch and then to the socket.

If a lamp does not work, first test the light bulb! Then plug the lamp into another socket in another room to see if it works there. If it does light, a single outlet or entire circuit may be out.

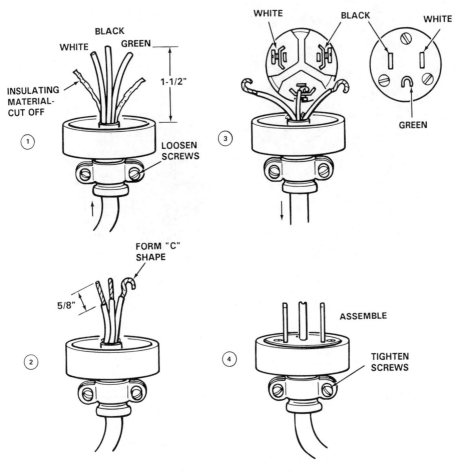

Figure 7-6.
Wiring a Three-Wire Plug

Unplug the lamp. Inspect the lamp wiring for obvious frays or breaks. Use a continuity tester (see Chapter 2) to test the wiring from each prong of the plug to the socket. There are two or three contacts in the socket, one or two at the bottom and one around the inside of the shell. The inside of the shell should always show continuity with one of the prongs on the plug. If there is one contact at the bottom of the socket, it should show continuity when the switch is on but should be open when the switch is off (see Figure 7-8). If there are two contacts at the bottom of the socket, the switch is a three-position switch using a "three-way" bulb. One position is off (no continuity on either contact). One position is low light (continuity on one contact). One position is medium light (continuity on the other contact). One position is high light (continuity on both bottom contacts).

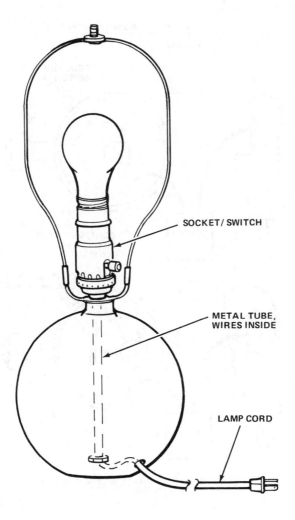

Figure 7-7.
Lamp Wiring

If the switch does not work, the entire socket/switch assembly may have to be replaced. You can find replacement socket/switches at most hardware stores. First, make certain the lamp is unplugged from the wall socket. Lift off the socket shell by pressing in on the side of the shell as shown in Figure 7-9. Unscrew the two terminals on the socket to release the wires. You can now measure continuity between the plug and the two wires. If there is no continuity on one or two wires, the socket/switch is all right and the *wire* should be replaced. If there is continuity on both wires, the socket/switch will have to be replaced.

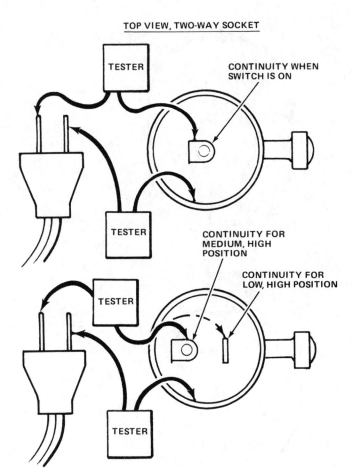

Figure 7-8.
Testing Lamp Wiring

To replace the socket/switch, substitute the new socket/switch for the old and fasten the wires under the terminal screws, being careful to avoid strands of wire that stick out from under the screw. Replace the socket/switch and test.

To replace the lamp wire, buy new lamp cord wire. To help route the wire through the lamp, splice the new wire to the old at the point where it comes through the shell by wrapping the wire ends together and using electrician's tape as shown in Figure 7-10. Pull the old cord from the plug end until the new cord comes through. Discard the old cord. Pull the length of cord you require on the lamp and put a plug on the end as described above.

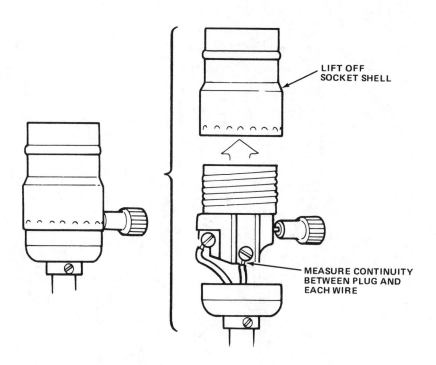

LIFT OFF
SOCKET SHELL

MEASURE CONTINUITY
BETWEEN PLUG AND
EACH WIRE

Figure 7-9.
Uncovering the Socket

On the socket end, tie an "Underwriter's knot" (see Figure 7-4) in the cord for strain relief. Cut the two wires about 1 1/2 inches from the knot. Strip about 5/8 inches from the end of each wire and fasten under the screw terminals, taking care that strands of wire do not stick out from under the screw heads. Replace the socket shell and light bulb and test.

Fluorescent Lights

Fluorescent lights are not connected to ac power directly, as shown in Figure 7-11. Instead, a transformer called a *ballast* is used to increase the 115 volts ac to an even greater voltage to power the lights. A device called a *starter* is used in some lights to help turn on the lights. On newer lights the starter is built into the ballast.

Light Does Not Light At All

Fluorescent lights may not operate if the room they are in is too cold. Raise the room temperature and try the lights again.

If a fluorescent light will not light, the first thing to look for is a burned out light. Replace the tube with the same type and length. Most tubes have two prongs

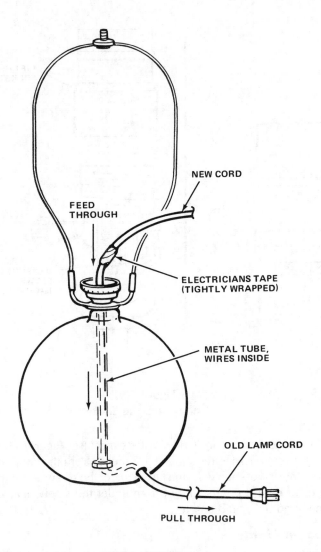

Figure 7-10.
Replacing Lamp Wire

on each end and are removed by twisting the tube and pulling it out. Make certain that the light switch is off before removing and inserting tubes.

If the light still does light after replacement of the tube, either the starter or the ballast may be out. Starters do not last much longer than the light tubes in many cases, so this is a good thing to try first. If there is a separate starter, find a replacement at your local hardware store and replace. Starters are removed by twisting counterclockwise and replaced by twisting clockwise.

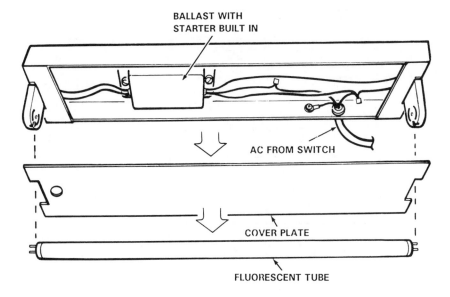

BALLAST WITH
STARTER BUILT IN

AC FROM SWITCH

COVER PLATE

FLUORESCENT TUBE

Figure 7-11.
Typical Fluorescent Light

Replacing the Ballast

Make certain the wall switch is off. It may be a good idea to also turn off the circuit breaker for the light if you know which one it is. Remove the tube and cover plate from the fluorescent fixture to expose the ballast. Before replacing the ballast, check the number of wires on the new ballast with the wires on the old ballast; they should be the same. Label the wires going to the ballast, as shown in Figure 7-12. Cut all wires leading to the old ballast, making the cuts close to the body of the ballast. Strip the ends of the wires about 5/8 inches. Remove the old ballast and mount the new one (usually with two screws). Cut off all but two inches of the new ballast wires. Strip these wires 5/8 inch. Using wire nuts (see "Wire Nuts" in Chapter 5), connect the new ballast wires to the existing wires.

Replace the cover plate, fluorescent tube, and test. If the light still does not work, call an electrician.

Other Symptoms

If the light blinks continuously, you probably need a new tube. If the ends of the tube are lighted but the center of the tube is not lighted, you probably need a new starter (or ballast if there is no separate starter).

Testing Smoke Alarms

Smoke alarms are one of two types. In new homes, smoke alarms are usually

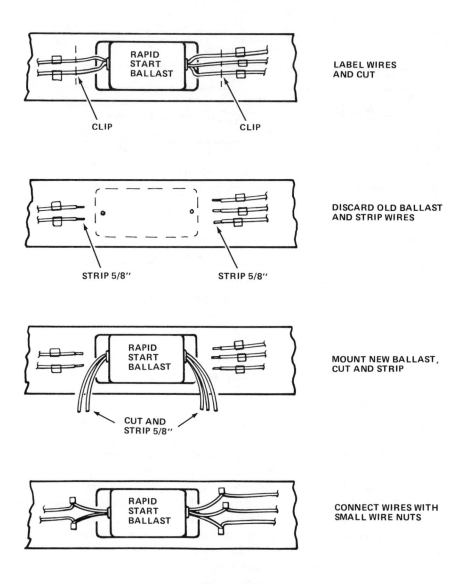

Figure 7-12.
Replacing the Ballast

operated by 115 volts ac and are connected in a junction box directly to a circuit in your home. Battery-operated smoke alarms do not require direct connection to the ac power circuits, but use a small battery that must be periodically replaced.

Ac-powered smoke alarms will not fail unless the electricity powering them fails. Some ac-powered smoke alarms have a small light that indicates power is being supplied to the unit. Almost all ac-powered smoke alarms have a "press to test" button, as shown in Figure 7-13. Press this button to see if the alarm signal sounds. If it does not sound, replace the alarm.

Battery-powered smoke alarms do not usually have a light, to conserve battery power. They do have a "press to test" button, however. Press the button to see if the alarm sounds. If it does not, replace the alarm. When battery power falls off, the battery-powered smoke alarm senses it and starts a short signal, usually a series of beeps, spaced seconds apart. When this happens, replace the battery in the alarm with one of the same type.

Concerned about your alarm working? Test it by blowing smoke at the alarm - a closely held lighted cigarette will work. Most alarms work not only by visible smoke, but *ionized air* as well - invisible combustion.

Testing Home Appliances

Home appliances used to be simple - a wall plug, electrical cord, a simple switch, and Nichrome wire for a toaster, for example. Today's appliances are increasingly more complicated and do not lend themselves to simple testing. Often a home appliance such as a toaster or sewing machine will include a small computer called a microprocessor. However, there are a few things you can look for in testing home appliances.

Figure 7-13.
Smoke Alarm Press to Test

First look at the power cord. If the appliance is dead, look for frayed wires. If the cord can be disconnected from the appliance (such as a frying pan) you can perform a continuity test of the cord. If the cord is open, replacement cords can be found at hardware stores.

Some audio equipment, video equipment, microwaves, and computers have fuses in the unit. Typically, these look like Figure 7-14. This figure shows types of *panel-mount* fuse holders with glass or ceramic fuses inside. The glass fuses show immediately whether the fuse is bad - the fuse is bad if the thin wire inside the fuse is open. Ceramic fuses are solid, but can be tested with a continuity tester or multitester.

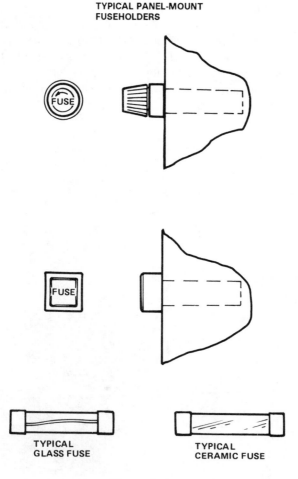

Figure 7-14.
Panel Mount Fuse Types

As in all devices with fuses, check *why* the fuse blew, and be prepared for the fuse to blow again. If it does, you'll need to have the appliance or device repaired by the factory or appliance repairman. Read the instruction manual to determine the proper type of fuse for replacement.

If the appliance is completely dead, it may be a faulty switch. If you can gain access to the switch, you can test it by using a multitester across the switch contacts. Switch types are many and varied, and include many custom-made switches specifically designed for the appliance. Also, some switches are speed or power controls, testing of which is beyond the scope of this book. Some appliances, however, may use the simple switches shown in Figure 7-15, or variations.

Depending upon the type of appliance, the resistance across the switch may be very low if the switch feeds a transformer or motor. However, there should be *some* change in the resistance when the switch is activated. If there is *no detectable change* the switch is probably bad. Remove one lead of the switch and test again, this time with a continuity tester. There should definitely be continuity with the switch in one position and no continuity with the switch in the other position. In replacing the switch, try to get an exact duplicate. Failing that, be sure to get a switch rated at 115 volts ac and a current rating equal to the power rating of the appliance divided by 115 (for example, a 345 watt appliance would require a switch with a rating of at least 345/115 = 3 amperes.

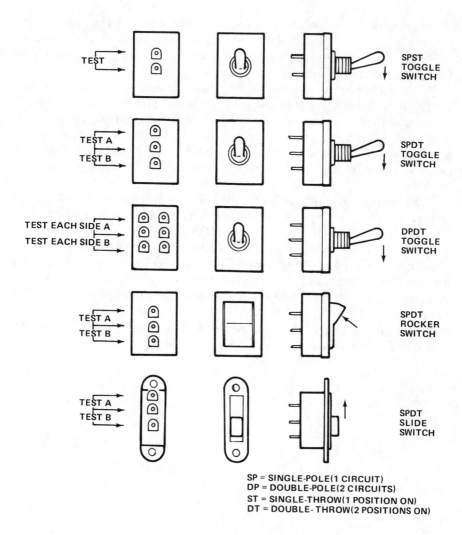

Figure 7-15.
Common Appliance Switch Types

Chapter 8
Testing Automotive Circuits

Automotive electrical systems are quite different than household electrical circuits in that electrical power other than ignition circuits is 12 volts direct current. This direct current power comes from a battery and a generator or alternator, which transforms energy stored from burning fuel. In this chapter we'll provide information on how to perform simple automotive testing on such a system to maintain your battery, test and replace lights, replace signal flashers, and test your car's radio.

Basic Automotive Electrical System

The basic automotive electrical system is shown in Figure 8-1. A *battery* provides power to turn a starter motor to turn the engine over. As the engine turns it rotates a *distributor* that sends spark current to the motor's spark plugs. The spark plugs create an electrical spark that ignites gasoline (or other fuel) in each cylinder of the engine. As the fuel is ignited, it pushes a piston in the cylinder down to provide power. Although the battery provides this initial starting action, once the engine has started, the motion of the engine is maintained by the distributor spark current routed to each spark plug and the constant firing of each spark plug to explode an air and fuel mixture in the cylinders. The spark current is created by a high-voltage (5000 to 20,000 volts) coil or electronic ignition circuit that transforms battery current.

When the engine is running from explosions of fuel in the cylinders, it not only drives the wheels of the car through gearing, but also rotates a *generator* or *alternator* shaft. The generator (older cars) or alternator is a small electrical generator that replenishes electrical energy drained from the battery and also provides current for spark plug and other electrical requirements of the car. The generator or alternator in conjunction with an electrical device called a *voltage regulator,* produces direct current, usually 12 volts dc or higher.

Among the devices other than spark plugs powered by the battery/alternator are small computers that control the engine firing, antiskid braking system, and other functions; headlights; parking lights; taillights; turn indicator lights; power windows; power roof; door locks; radio; audio system; and cellular car phone - in short, all electrical devices that the car uses.

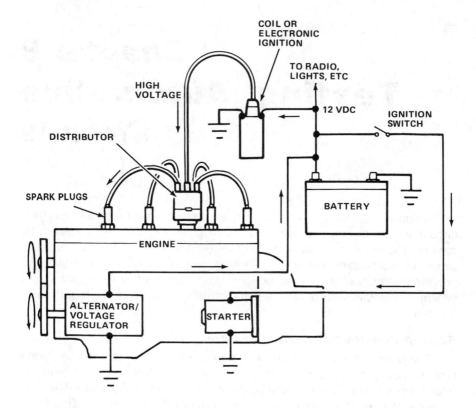

Figure 8-1.
Automotive Electrical System

Car Batteries

Older batteries were generally 6-volt batteries. However, newer automotive systems use 12-volt batteries. A car battery is made up of six *cells* in a 12-volt battery, each cell producing about two volts of electrical potential. Each cell has plates made up of two different metals - lead and lead peroxide. The plates are immersed in water and sulfuric acid. The water and sulfuric action mixture acts on the plates to produce a *charge* on the plates. One terminal of the battery is a positive terminal (+) (containing an abundance of charge) while the other terminal is a negative terminal (-), containing a shortage of charge. The charge is electrical current waiting to happen. When a wire is connected between the two terminals, electrical direct current (dc) flows.

Starting a car requires a great deal of energy. In cold weather, for example, a typical starting current is 300 amperes. A typical battery when fully charged can supply this much current for at least 40 seconds. (This represents 3,600 watts of power for a short time!) As this current flows out of the battery, the battery is *discharged.* Normally, the generator or alternator in a car or truck generates enough current to handle the electrical needs of the car and also recharge the battery. However, if the battery is low on the water and sulfuric acid mixture, if the temperature is cold, or the battery is simply old, the amount of charge it can hold diminishes. There's another thing that serves to reduce the current the battery can supply as well - bad connections on or from the battery.

A fully charged battery may measure as much as 14.4 volts and as low as 10.6 volts when discharged. The nominal voltage is about 12.6 volts.

Testing Car Batteries

A *hydrometer* measures a quality called the specific gravity of the water and sulfuric acid mixture in the battery. Inexpensive hydrometers are available in hardware and automotive parts stores. However, another way to measure the amount of charge your battery has is with a multitester. Turn off the car, set the multitester to DCV and measure across the terminals of the battery. A charged battery should measure in the vicinity of 12.6 volts dc when all electrical devices are turned off in the car. If the battery measures a great deal lower than that it may not be charging properly. Some of the possible reasons for not charging are:

- Water and sulfuric acid mixture low

- Old battery

- Corroded contacts on battery

- Faulty regulator or alternator

SAFETY NOTE

The water and sulfuric acid mixture found in a battery can be harmful to your eyes or skin. Wear protective eyewear when working around an automotive battery. IMMEDIATELY wash off the mixture if it comes in contact with your eyes or skin.

When an automotive battery operates, it produces hydrogen and oxygen gas. Hydrogen gas is extremely flammable. NEVER smoke while working around or over a battery.

Avoid overcharging a battery. Overcharging may damage the battery and create a good deal of heat and gases.

Test the water and sulfuric acid mixture in a battery by measuring the height. Some battery cases are now made of a plastic material through which the water and sulfuric acid level can be seen. Each cell in the battery may have a cap which can be unscrewed as well, to allow you to see the level. (However, many "sealed" batteries have one or two larger cover assemblies which lift off to expose the cells.) If the water and sulfuric acid level is low, add *distilled water* to bring the level up close to the top of the cell. Avoid overfilling.

There are two battery terminal posts on a battery, as shown in Figure 8-2. One of the terminals is negative (-) and the other is positive (+). The terminals are marked on the top of the battery. One of the terminals is attached by a short, heavy cable to the frame of the car. This is known as the *ground* of the battery. If the negative terminal is connected to the frame of the car, the electrical system is known as *negative ground*. If the positive terminal is connected, the electrical system is known as *positive ground*. Most modern electrical systems are *negative ground*. The other battery cable is connected to other parts of the electrical system, such as the starter and ignition switch.

If the battery connections are corroded or loose, the battery current may be reduced. An indication of this is dimming of the lights and a click when you try to start the motor. To clean the connections, make a mixture of a small amount of baking soda and water and pour it over the battery cable connections. Wipe with a rag. Be careful not to get any of the corrosion products on you as they may be acidic and harmful to your eyes and skin. Loosen the bolt or screw securing the battery cable and remove the cable or cables. Clean and wipe any remaining corrosion from the battery connection. Use sandpaper to renew the connections if necessary. Replace the cable and tighten. Avoid over tightening. Protect the connection with petroleum jelly or lithium grease.

Jump Starting Your Car or Truck

Most cars or trucks can be "jump started" by using a battery in another car or truck, connected by "booster" cables to your car or truck. Read your car's owner's

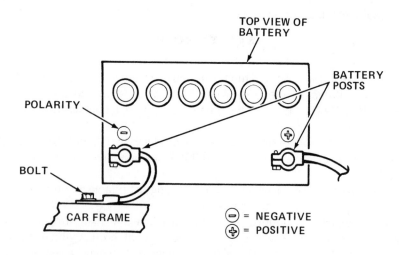

Figure 8-2.
Battery Terminal Posts

manual to see what exact procedure should be followed. Here is a procedure that will work in many cases:

The battery in the second car or truck must be the same voltage as your car or truck - usually 12 volts. You'll need two heavy battery jumper cables - at least 10 gauge wire (4 or 6 gauge is better) with clamps on each end. This example assumes your vehicle has a negative ground.

Move the second car or truck close to your vehicle, but not touching. If they touch, a premature contact might be established. Turn the ignition on your vehicle off. With the motor running on the second car or truck, clamp a jumper cable on the *positive* terminal of the second vehicle's battery. Clamp the other end of the cable to the *positive* terminal of your battery. Clamp another cable to the *negative* terminal of the second vehicle's battery. Clamp the other end of the cable to the frame of your vehicle but not to any part of the fuel system.

Speed up the engine of the second vehicle to increase the voltage available at the battery terminals. Start the engine of your vehicle. When your vehicle starts, remove the clamp from the *frame* of your vehicle first, and then from the negative terminal of the second vehicle. Now remove the other clamp from your *positive* terminal and then from the second vehicle's battery.

How to Recharge Your Battery

One way to recharge your battery is to top off the water and sulfuric acid solution using distilled water, check the cable connections, and then start the car, getting a "jump start" if necessary. Drive the car for one half hour or so - the longer the better. If the battery is in good condition and the alternator and voltage regulator are working properly, the battery should be at least partially recharged after the drive. Avoid battery drain (starts and stops) until the car can be driven an additional time.

Another method for recharging your battery is to use a *battery charger*. The battery charger reverses the battery process. The battery charger forces a current in the opposite direction into your battery, building up a charge as it does so. Battery chargers can be purchased from most hardware stores. A typical battery charger is shown in Figure 8-3.

Before plugging in the charger, connect the positive clamp of the charger (usually red or marked with a +) to the positive terminal of the battery. Connect the negative clamp of the charger (usually black or marked with a -) to the negative terminal of the battery. Set the voltage switch on the charger (if there is one) to 12 Volts. Now plug in the charger and turn on the power switch. (This avoids a possible spark if the charger is turned on.) Typical battery chargers have a meter showing the amount of charge. Initially the needle on the meter will be well over to the right, showing charge (about 4 or 5 amps), but will fall off rapidly. If the meter needle does not fall off after an hour or so, the battery may have a failed cell and may not be able to be recharged. Allow the battery to recharge for four or five hours, or until the needle drops to about 2 amps. Before removing the battery clamps, unplug the charger from the wall outlet and *then* remove the clamps.

Figure 8-3.
Battery Recharger

After the battery has been recharged, it should show a higher voltage reading - about 13 volts or more.

How Wires Are Routed in a Car or Truck

As mentioned above, the terminal of the battery that is connected to the frame of the car or truck establishes the ground of the electrical system. Usually the negative battery terminal will be connected, establishing a negative ground system. Almost all wiring in a car or truck uses one wire - the other wire is the metal frame of the car or truck. This is done to save money, but also to avoid a larger *voltage drop* due to the resistance found in any wire.

In troubleshooting electrical parts such as car lights, therefore, you'll typically see a single wire going to one terminal of the light or device. The other terminal of the device will be connected to the nearest ground with a short wire or terminal.

Fuse Blocks

When wires are routed through a car or truck they are bundled together in a *cable*, rather than as individual wires. These cables are known as wiring harnesses. There may be many wires in each harness.

Like home wiring, car or truck wiring divides the wiring into *circuits*. There may be a circuit for the air conditioning wiring, for example, another for stop lights, and another for power windows. Sometimes the functions are somewhat mixed together as in the case of a lighter, radio, and rear window wiper.

Also like home wiring, the circuits are protected with *fuses*. Automotive fuses are generally put together in one place called a *fuse block*. This is for ease of access. A typical fuse block is shown in Figure 8-4. In newer model cars, the fuse block is generally marked with a legend telling what circuit the fuse is for and what current the fuse can carry.

Fuses come in different styles, depending upon the make of car: flat-bladed fuses, ceramic fuses, and glass cartridge fuses. The different types are shown in Figure 8-5. Most fuses are color coded to represent the current they can carry.

When a light, motor, or other function fails on a car or truck, one of the first things you should examine is the appropriate fuse. Of course, if a fuse does fail it may signal a short or overload that will recur, just as in home wiring. Remove the fuse block cover, if there is one, or pull down the fuse block and examine all fuses. If in doubt about a fuse (they may be hard to see in engine compartments) pull the fuse out for a closer examination. Replace a blown fuse with a fuse of the same rating. NEVER use a fuse with a higher rating - it may result in overheating of a wire and potential fire.

Some fuses, especially the ones used in early VW cars, are prone to corrosion. Remove the fuse and clean the ends of the fuse and fuse holder with fine sandpaper.

Figure 8-4.
Typical Car Fuse Block

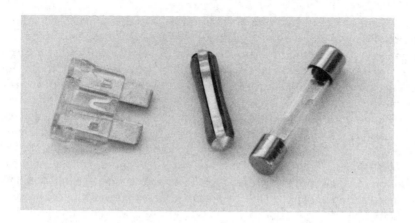

Figure 8-5.
Automotive Fuses

Fusible Links

In addition to fuses, cars and trucks have *fusible links*. These are heavy duty fuses that fail in catastrophic conditions that cause short circuits, such as accidents. They are usually installed between battery and starter or battery and fuse panel. If they fail, all power in the car will be turned off. They need to be replaced.

Circuit Breakers

In addition to fuses, some circuits in cars have *circuit breakers*. These are usually not as easily located in cars as the fuse blocks. The circuit breakers in some cases reset automatically and may result in turning the circuit off and on. For example, headlight circuits normally have a built-in circuit breaker. If the headlight circuit overloads, the circuit breaker may turn off and then turn on again, overload, and then turn off again, and so forth. The result is flashing headlights. The basic idea is that flashing headlights are a great deal safer than headlights that go completely dark when a fuse blows!

Replacing Lights in Cars and Trucks

There are three general types of light bulbs used in cars and trucks: *bayonet* type bulbs for taillights and turn signals, bulbs for interior lights, and sealed-beam headlights. In all cases, check the fuse block to make certain no fuses are blown before testing individual bulbs.

Bayonet Bulbs

Typical bayonet light bulbs are shown in Figure 8-6. These bulbs are removed and inserted by a twist and lock action. In most vehicles, you may have to remove a covering assembly to get at the bulbs from the rear (inside the trunk, for example). A bulb holder is then removed and you can twist out the bulb. Replace the bulb with an exact replacement from an auto parts store or car dealership. To

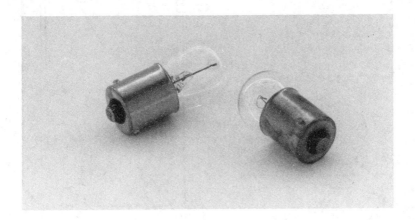

Figure 8-6.
Typical Bayonet Bulbs

test the bulb, measure the continuity with a continuity tester or multitester between the base contact and side, as shown in Figure 8-7. If the bulb is bad, there will be no continuity.

Interior Light Bulbs

Interior light bulbs may be of the bayonet type, but also may be a cylindrical or other type as shown in Figure 8-8. These bulbs are replaced by removing a cover, snapping out the old bulb and snapping in a new bulb. The new bulb should be an exact replacement. Like the bayonet bulbs, these bulbs can be tested with a continuity tester or multitester.

Headlights

Headlights are now *sealed beams*, units that incorporate light bulb filaments and a reflector in a single sealed unit. There are several types of headlights, a two-headlight system that has both a "high" and "low" beam, a four-headlight system that has only one beam per light, and a four-headlight system with two lights having both high and low beams. Replace headlights when the entire light is out on a two-headlight system or when either beam is out on a four-headlight system. As described above, flashing headlights indicate an overload somewhere in the headlight circuit which you may need to have looked at by a mechanic. Headlights are easily replaced by unplugging a connector which can only be plugged in one way, replacing the sealed beam, and then plugging in the con-

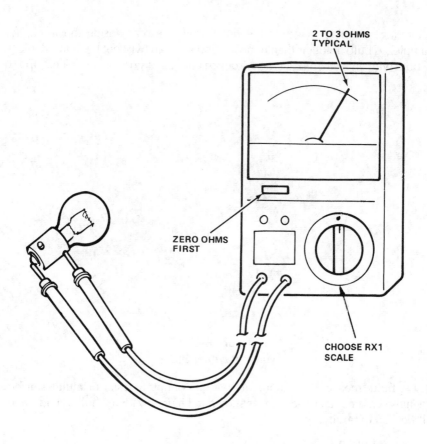

Figure 8-7.
Testing a Bulb

nector again. When headlights are replaced, they may require adjustment so that the beam shines properly down the road.

Turn Signals and Hazard Flashers

Turn signals and hazard flashers are similar. Turn signal flashers are small units (see Figure 8-9) that turn either the right or left turn signal lights on and off. Current flowing through the unit heats up contact points which then turn the unit off. Hazard flashers blink all four turn signal lights on and off. Hazard flashers are designed to operate even if one or more turn signal lights are burned out.

If a turn signal turns on and stays on, there's a good chance that either the front or rear turn signal light is burned out. Current through just one light isn't normally enough to turn off the flasher.

If turn signals or hazard lights do not flash or are erratic, there's a good chance the flasher needs replacement. However, check the fuse for lights that won't turn on at all. Turn signal and hazard flashers are often accessible and can be replaced without having to go to a mechanic. Be sure to use an exact replacement. The units usually just pull directly out and plug directly in - it's impossible to plug them in the wrong way. Be sure to replace them with the car ignition turned off.

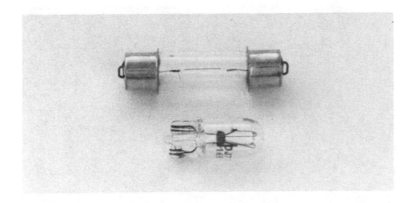

Figure 8-8.
Interior Light Bulbs

Auto Radios

One common problem is a "dead" radio or one with extremely low volume. Check the antenna connection. Car radios need an outside antenna for reception, and if the cable has come loose, the radio will appear to be dead or have very little audio. Another problem might be a faulty cable to the antenna. Car radio antennas are often connected with a plug as shown in Figure 8-10. The center lead of this plug is connected to the exterior antenna, and the outside "shield" lead is connected to the car body. Both connections should show continuity when tested with a continuity tester or multitester.

Another common problem is a damaged or scratchy-sounding speaker. Usually this is the result of playing the radio at loud volume for extended periods of time. Speakers are generally four- or eight-ohm *impedance* - a measure of the speaker's resistance to the alternating currents found in audio signals. The impedance of the speaker is usually marked on the speaker; replace the speaker with one having the same physical size, same impedance, and same *power rating*. The power rating is in watts and may be marked on the speaker. If not, refer to your owner's manual for the radio to find out the maximum output in watts per channel. Use a speaker with a power rating equal to or higher than this. Auto radio speakers can be found at Radio Shack.

Figure 8-9.
Typical Turn Signal Flasher

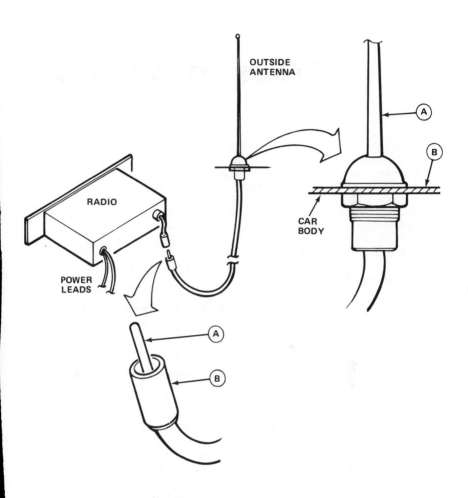

Figure 8-10.
Car Antenna Connections

Glossary of Terms

Ac - Alternating current. Usually refers to the 115-volt ac power found in most homes, although may refer to low-voltage ac power from a transformer.

Alkaline battery - One of the better types of batteries. Long lasting.

Alternator - Small electrical generator in a car or truck driven by the motor.

Amp (or ampere) - Unit of current.

Analog multitester - A multitester with a dial rather than a digital readout.

Audio cables - Shielded cables used for stereos and sound systems.

Autoranging multitester - A multitester in which the device senses the voltage or resistance range to be used. There are no range selection knobs to be set.

AWG - American Wire Gauge. A standard grading for wire diameter. Smaller numbers indicate larger diameter wires and vice versa.

Battery - A device that produces energy by chemical reaction.

Battery tester - An inexpensive device to test batteries by showing a "Good" or "Replace" indication.

Bayonet bulb - A common type of automotive bulb.

Blow - To melt a fuse's link so that no current can flow.

Carbon-zinc battery - A common type of battery.

Circuit analyzer - Device that plugs into an electrical outlet and verifies the proper wiring of the outlet.

Circuit breaker - A device that opens up when excessive current flows. It can be reset by pushing in a button or throwing a switch.

Conductor - A material that offers little resistance to the flow of electrical current, such as copper or iron.

Continuity tester - An inexpensive device to test whether a length of wire is unbroken.

Current - The flow of electricity through a wire. Can be compared to water through a pipe. Measured in amperes.

Dc - Direct current. Refers to the dc power obtained from a battery or power supply.

Digital multitester - A multitester with a digital readout rather than a dial.

Doorbell wire - Small diameter wire used in low-voltage doorbell circuits.

Edison base fuse - An early type of fuse still used in older home wiring today.

Fluorescent light - A light that illuminates by glowing gas. Usually in the shape of a long tube.

Fuse - Device that limits the flow of current by melting when excessive current flows in a circuit.

Fuse block - A block of fuses found in a car. Similar to fuse box for house wiring.

Fuse box - See Power panel.

Fusible link - A fuse made of heavier wire that melts in emergency conditions in a car if excessive current flows.

GFCI - See Ground fault circuit interrupter.

GFI - See Ground fault circuit interrupter.

Ground - A common wire that completes the circuit. An earth ground is made by water pipes or damp floors.

Ground fault circuit interrupter - A sensitive circuit breaker that rapidly switches off power when a too much current flows in a bathroom, kitchen, outside or basement outlet, or other area with a water and grounding hazard.

Ground wire - A wire that carries no current but is connected to ground.

Grounded outlet - An ac power outlet in which the junction box and outlet frame is connected to the ground wire of the system.

Hazard flasher - The device in a vehicle that flashes the four turn signal lights on and off.

"Hot" - A wire connected to 115 volts ac or high voltage.

Hot wire - A wire that is not a neutral wire but has a 115 volts ac present. Usually black.

Impedance - A type of alternating current resistance. Used to classify speakers.

Insulator - A material that offers very high resistance to flow of electrical current, such as glass or plastic.

Intermittent closure - A condition in which a wire or switch closes for a brief period of time.

Jump start - To start a car by connecting the battery from another car by means of cables. Used for dead battery conditions.

Lantern battery - A large type of battery found in lantern-type flashlights.

Latch - An action in which a brief closure or opening sets an on state signaling that the closing or opening occurred, even though it may have been too short to have been noticed by eye.

mAh - Milliampere hours. A measure of how much energy can be stored in a battery. The greater the number of mAh, the better.

Multimeter - See "Multitester".

Multitester - A testing device that can measure voltage, resistance, and sometimes current.

Negative ground - An automotive system in which the negative pole of the battery is grounded.

Neutral wire - A wire that is common with ground. Less dangerous than the hot wire, but can still carry voltage in some miswired homes. Usually white.

Nickel-cadmium battery - A common rechargeable battery.

Normally closed - A circuit that has one or more switches in series that are closed unless opened by some event.

Normally open - A circuit that has one or more switches in parallel that are open unless closed by some event.

Ohm's Law - A basic electrical rule that says that current in amperes equals voltage in volts divided by resistance in ohms.

Open circuit - A condition in which there is a break in a wire supplying power.

Power - The amount of energy that a device uses. A high-power device consumes more energy than a low-power device. Measured in watts.

Power panel (or Fuse box) - The main box in your home that connects home wiring to the wiring from your power company.

Power supply - (Usually) a device that converts 115 volts ac into low-voltage direct current similar to that found in batteries.

Resistance - The amount of resistance to the flow of current through a wire. Can be compared to small diameter or large diameter water hoses. Measured in ohms.

S fuse - An improved Edison type fuse used in home wiring.

Screw base fuse - A household fuse that is screwed into a receptacle to provide power in a circuit.

Sealed beam - The usual type of auto headlight which uses a sealed filament(s) with a reflector.

Shield - The outer braided wire found on many audio and video cables.

Short circuit - (Or "short") A condition in which a hot wire and ground or common wire touch and excessive current flows.

Solid wire - A common type of copper wire found in household wiring and other applications. Used where the wire is not subjected to much bending.

Stranded wire - A common type of copper wire found in low-voltage wiring. The wire is made up of many small-diameter strands twisted together.

Three-way switch - A switch used in a two-switch circuit in which each switch can control a light or outlet.

Time delay fuse - A fuse that allows a momentary surge of current without blowing.

Transformer - A device to convert high-voltage to low-voltage or vice versa. Works only on alternating current power.

Transistor battery - A battery originally used in transistor radios, but now found in many devices.

Turn signal flasher - The device in a car that flashes the turn signals.

Volt - Unit of voltage.

Voltage - The amount of electrical "pressure" that pushes current through a wire. Can be compared to water pressure. Measured in volts.

Voltage regulator - A device in an automotive system which recharges the battery and regulates voltage from the generator or alternator.

Watt - Unit of power.

Wire nuts - A device that is used to connect two or more wires by twisting them inside a small insulated cone.

Zinc-chloride battery - A better type of battery.

Index